THE SPY WHO SWAPPED SHOES

Stephen Fletcher Thrillers Book One

Geoffrey Davison

SAPERE
BOOKS

THE SPY WHO
SWAPPED SHOES

Published by Sapere Books.

11 Bank Chambers, Hornsey, London, N8 7NN,
United Kingdom

saperebooks.com

ISBN: 978-1-913028-95-4

To M.G. & N.

Chapter One

A release of steam from the powerful engine shrieked its impatient warning across the dimly-lit platforms of Istanbul Station. From a side entrance to the station, a man approached the platform where the Istanbul-Vienna train was standing. He hesitated for a moment, brushed off the rain from his dark raincoat, pulled down the brim of his hat and moved unnoticed past a small group of bystanders and entered a first-class carriage.

Inside the carriage, he was met by a white-coated Serbian attendant, who glanced at his reserved seat list and, without comment, directed the man to a window seat in one of the compartments. The man placed his suitcase and hat on the rack. Without glancing around the compartment, he took his seat and stared out of the window at the dark, dirty tiled walls of the station. Occasionally, his hand came up to his face and fingered a small scar on his neck above his collar. This unconscious movement was followed by the man touching his moustache and adjusting his spectacles, as if they were unfamiliar to him.

The carriage door opened and from the reflection in the window the man could see the large, portly figure of a Patriarch of the Greek Orthodox Church, in his long black robes, enter the compartment. The Patriarch puffed his way through the narrow entrance door, placed his case on the rack and took his seat alongside the man in the corner. His build was such that he overflowed his allotted space and almost hid the man in the corner from the view of anyone in the corridor.

The man shrank further into the corner in an effort to disengage himself from the Patriarch, but didn't even look up at his companion. If he had, he would have seen little of the Patriarch's face, for it was covered with a large, flowing, white beard, tinted with stains of yellow around his mouth. The Patriarch's hat almost touched the luggage rack and he sat with eyes half closed, his large brown rough hands clasped together on his lap.

Again the carriage door opened and two further passengers entered. The first was a Turk, a small man, with stubbly grey hair and a walrus moustache. His face was leathery looking and wizened. He placed his case on the rack and sat alongside the Patriarch.

Following him into the compartment was a woman. She was small in stature and her grey hair and drab clothes gave her a matronly appearance. She had a round, demure, homely face and as she entered the compartment she smiled at her companions. Her overtures, however, got no response and she placed her own suitcase on the rack and took up the seat in the opposite corner by the window. From a large handbag she produced some knitting and proceeded to manipulate the needles as if the transportation from her previous location to her present position had been an irritating interruption in the more serious necessity of completing her task.

The man in the corner pulled his raincoat sleeve over his wrist and continued to stare out of the window. He had been aware of the other passengers entering the compartment, but he was more concerned about the foul, overpowering odour which flowed from the large figure of the Patriarch. The nauseating smell of garlic and perspiration was becoming unbearable and it was a great relief to him when the Turk lit a cigar and the evil smelling fumes eventually bypassed the Patriarch.

The passengers sat in silence and only shuffled in their seat when the guard's whistle gave the engine driver his long awaited signal to jerk the train into motion. The train slowly left the station, impatiently puffing smoke and gradually building up speed.

From his window seat the man could see little of the town of Istanbul except for an occasional glimpse of the narrow cobbled streets and a vintage tram car. The minareted temples were all hidden by the dusk and rain. He allowed himself a quick glance around the compartment. It was a non-sleeping compartment with the normal two rows of seats. It had no refinements to indicate that it was a first-class compartment — it was purely functional. The only feature decorating the wall was a small map indicating the route the train was to take. Istanbul to Plovdiv and Sofia in Bulgaria, through the western tip of Romania to Belgrade in Hungary and on to Vienna. A journey through a tunnel in the Iron Curtain. The man recoiled further in his seat and closed his eyes.

For nearly an hour and a half they sat motionless, listening to the rhythmic sound of the wheels on the track, each to their own thoughts, but as the train started to reduce speed there was an unspoken, unconscious, tenseness in the atmosphere. They were approaching the Bulgarian border. The Turk lit another cigar, the Patriarch appeared to increase in size and the elderly lady manipulated her needles with increased speed. The only person who seemed unmoved was the man in the corner who appeared to be asleep.

The inspection by the Turkish officials was a mere formality, but when they crossed into Bulgaria they found the Communists approached the task in a more serious and sinister manner. The station was suddenly illuminated by powerful arc lamps and along both platforms stood a row of armed soldiers. A tannoy bellowed out a message in five different languages informing the passengers that the train would stop at Plovdiv and Sofia and warning them against alighting from the train unless they had a permit to enter the Republic.

From the passport inspection the man in the corner gained a certain amount of information about his other companions. The elderly lady was Frau Sleisser, an Austrian and she was returning to her home in Vienna. The Turk was also going to Vienna on what he described as 'cigar business'. The Patriarch was Greek, but his destination remained a secret.

It was a further thirty minutes before the train was allowed to proceed. As they were pulling away from the station, the man in the corner glanced at his watch — it was 8.50 p.m. — they were running behind schedule. He sighed and closed his eyes, not that he intended to sleep, but to prevent any of his companions engaging him in conversation. He kept his pose off and on for the next two hours, until the compartment door was suddenly pulled to one side and the white-coated Serbian attendant entered the compartment.

'We shall be in Plovdiv in two minutes,' he said in subdued tones. He spoke in Turkish, but repeated his remark in German. 'We are stopping to pick up a passenger. No-one must leave the train.' Again he repeated his remark in German. There was no response from any of the passengers and he hurriedly made his exit and closed the compartment door.

The man in the corner peered out of the window to catch a glimpse of the town, but all he could see were the dark forms of the railway buildings as they approached the station. The Austrian lady had stopped knitting and was holding her needles quite still in her hands. She was looking straight ahead of her, but seeing nothing. She was deep in thought. The Patriarch remained motionless, his eyes closed, but the man noticed his big fat hands were clasped together, tightly gripping each other, with white knuckles. The Turk was beyond his vision, but by the amount of cigar smoke which was entering the atmosphere, it was apparent that he was not asleep.

Voices were heard on the platform outside their carriage and the carriage door was opened. After a pause, it was closed again with a clash and footsteps approached the compartment along the corridor. The Austrian lady carried on with her knitting and the Patriarch's hands relaxed their grip.

As their compartment door was pulled to one side, the train continued with its interrupted journey and the man in the corner gave his full attention to the dark silhouetted buildings outside.

The Serbian attendant entered the compartment.

'This is your seat, Comrade,' he said, indicating one of the reserved seats. He accepted a case from someone in the corridor and placed it on the rack. He stood aside as a man entered the compartment, heavily muffled and wearing a thick, navy blue, belted gabardine raincoat and navy blue trilby hat. The man took off his hat and sat on the seat. On his knee was a briefcase, over which he placed his hat.

A Bulgarian soldier also entered the compartment and a whispered conversation took place with the passenger. The soldier withdrew from the compartment and took up a position outside in the corridor. The attendant followed the soldier out and closed the compartment door.

The man in the corner kept his eyes away from the latest passenger and returned to his feigned sleeping pose. If he had studied the man, he would have noticed they were very much alike. They were both just under six feet in height, of medium build, both had dark hair parted and waved in precisely the same position. They both had sallow faces and dark blue eyes and dark eyebrows. Even their noses were similar with a slight bump where it joined the brow and the same scar on the neck. But the moustache and glasses gave the man in the corner an older and more studious appearance.

Presently, he heard the sliding compartment doors of the carriage being opened and closed and the voice of the attendant passing on information. He waited patiently for the Serb to enter their compartment.

'We shall be entering the Plovdiv tunnel in five minutes,' the attendant announced in Turkish. 'We shall be in the tunnel for approximately thirty minutes. You are advised to draw your blinds. We shall be passing the Istanbul express before we leave the tunnel.' Again he repeated his remarks in German and for the benefit of the latest passenger, in a pidgin form of Bulgarian.

The Austrian lady thanked the attendant and pulled her blind and also the one of the centre window. The man in the corner, not understanding either Turkish, German, or Bulgarian, made no move, so the Patriarch, who had been awakened from his sleep by the opening and closing of the doors, stretched over the man without any apologies and pulled the corner blind.

The Turk pulled the blinds of the corridor window and the compartment door. He moved over to close the blind beside the man who had recently entered the compartment, but the man gave a brusque, 'No'. The Turk shrugged and returned to his seat.

The Serbian attendant returned his trek along the corridors and engaged the soldier standing outside the compartment in conversation. Two minutes later the train thundered into the tunnel with a deafening roar.

The train's entry into the tunnel appeared to be a signal for a change of attitude by the four original occupants. The Austrian lady carefully replaced her knitting in her handbag, the Turk stamped out his cigar and the man in the corner turned his attention past the latest passenger to join them to the corridor and noticed that the soldier had been enticed away from his post by the attendant.

The Patriarch slowly stood up and turned to his case on the rack, allowing his cloak to overlap the Turk. The Turk quickly leant forward and extracted a small calibre pistol, with silencer, from within the Patriarch's cloak and as the Patriarch turned to take his seat again, fired two quick shots at the man sitting opposite him. The muffled 'Plop, Plop,' sounded ridiculously innocent, but produced the desired effect and the man slumped forward — dead — with two small bullets embedded in his skull.

Chapter Two

The assassination, although sudden, produced no surprised screams or reactions from the other passengers, but immediately the compartment became a hive of activity.

The Turk pushed the dead man back against his seat and from his pocket produced a sharp pointed dagger. With this instrument he set about cutting the dead man's briefcase away from a chain which was fastened to his wrist. The Patriarch had taken the Turk's previous seat and was casting occasional glances behind the curtain at the soldier talking to the attendant. The man who had been sitting in the corner window seat had taken off his glasses and was carefully peeling off a false moustache. Without any further hesitation or modesty he started to strip off his clothes. The Austrian lady was studying the dead man's features and casting occasional glances from him to the man stripping off his clothes.

The Turk freed the briefcase and with his dagger split it open. He handed it over to the Patriarch and lifted the dead man over to the corner window seat. Quickly, with the help of the Austrian lady, he took off the raincoat and handed it to the man, who was now naked. The man slipped it on and rushed over to the dead man's seat. He pulled the coat about him and glanced along the corridor. The soldier was about four yards away from him, talking to the attendant.

The Turk and the Austrian lady quickly stripped the clothes off the dead body, handing each garment to the Patriarch, who passed them over to the man opposite. Silently, quickly, as a well-rehearsed drill, garment by garment exchanged bodies, starting at the feet and working upwards, all the time the dark raincoat hiding the man's movements. It took several minutes, but eventually the man was fully clothed — not carefully or correctly, but this could be adjusted later. He was sufficiently attired to impersonate the dead man.

The two wardrobe mistresses set about dressing the dead body in the other man's clothes. Meanwhile, the Patriarch had produced another briefcase from his personage, similar to the one taken from the dead man. He extracted the documents from the rifled briefcase, examined them, substituted alternatives where necessary and placed them in the new case. He fastened the lock and leant forward.

The man opposite took a quick glance through the corridor window, saw that the soldier was still occupied and also leant forward. From his wrist he unwrapped a length of small link chain. He handed the free end to the Patriarch, who put the special end fitting into the lock of the briefcase and, with a key, locked the chain and the briefcase together. The man sat back in his seat, the briefcase chained to his wrist and like his predecessor, sat with his trilby covering the case on his knee.

The Patriarch brought out a watch.

'Hurry,' he whispered in Turkish.

The Austrian lady fastened the laces of the dead man's shoes and turned to the Patriarch.

'The eyebrows,' she said.

The Patriarch nodded his head and said, 'Later.'

They completed their task and slumped the dead body, fully clothed, against the corner seat.

'The chain on the wrist,' the Austrian lady whispered urgently.

The Turk looked at the Patriarch, who again examined his watch. The Patriarch gave him the go ahead signal and the Turk got hold of the dead man's wrist, wrapped it in a fold of the raincoat and with his dagger, butchered the chain and briefcase handle away from the wrist.

The Patriarch stood up, his large, portly figure filling the gangway between the two rows of seats. He glanced at the man watching the corridor, who indicated that the soldier was still occupied. The Patriarch moved forward and lifted the blind of the large centre window. The Turk cleaned his dagger as the Patriarch slowly opened the window. The sudden intake of air bellowed the Patriarch's robes around the compartment and the train thundered along the track with an alarming and deafening clanging.

Hurriedly, the Patriarch stood back and the Turk desperately bundled the dead man out of the window. Immediately he closed the window again and pulled the blind. The contrasting dulled noise brought a sigh of relief from the Austrian lady. The Patriarch and the Turk sat down again.

The roar of an approaching train came rushing towards them and screamed past at high speed, causing their carriage to rock violently. The four passengers looked at one another, but said nothing. The Turk lit another cigar and relaxed in his seat, satisfied. The Patriarch wiped the perspiration from his brow.

Presently he spoke to the Austrian lady.

'The eyebrows,' he said in Turkish, this obviously being the common tongue.

'They extend too far across his face,' she explained in a subdued tone. 'I will have to shorten them.'

The Patriarch looked at the man opposite him. To the laymen he looked the actual image of the man who had been assassinated. But they weren't dealing with laymen, they had waited too long for this opportunity, it had to be as near perfect as possible.

'Is he still being looked after?' he said.

The man gave a glance along the corridor.

'Yes,' he replied. 'The Serb has done his job well.'

The Patriarch stood up and exchanged seats with the Austrian lady. She opened her large handbag and extracted a small bottle of colourless liquid and cotton wool. The man opposite leant forward and she dabbled some of the liquid on the ends of his eyebrows.

'It will take a minute to have effect,' she whispered.

The man leant back and the Austrian lady unwrapped a set of small instruments, selected one and placed the remainder back in her bag. She motioned the man forward again and with slow, deft, expert strokes, shaved off the ends of his eyebrows.

She sat back and examined his face critically. The scar on the neck and the build-up of the nose had healed without any trace of surgery. The shortening of the eyebrows had been the final touch of an expert. She felt satisfied that she had done her job well. No-one would be able to detect any difference from his appearance.

'Perfect,' she said and returned to her window seat.

The train left the tunnel and for a period of time they travelled in silence, content that their first hurdle was successful. But the Patriarch, who appeared to be in charge of the operations, became impatient and he signalled to the man opposite that they must continue with their programme. The man understood. He stood up and opened the carriage door.

The soldier quickly turned round. The man looked him square in the face and said in Bulgarian: 'I do not want to be disturbed, I am going to have a sleep. If I am not awake by the time we approach the border, you must call me.'

'Yes, Comrade, I understand,' the soldier replied, in a rough country accent.

The man closed the door, sat down again by the side of the corridor window and pulled down his blind.

The Patriarch waited a few moments and then spoke to him in hushed tones.

'The likeness is perfect,' he said, 'and the documents are in order.'

The man gave a wry smile. 'Good,' he whispered. 'It has worked out well.' The two men looked hard at each other. They were friends, they had worked together for many years, but this was the parting of the ways. The Patriarch appeared reluctant to proceed, but finally said, 'Anything before we continue?'

The man leant forward and said in almost inaudible tones, 'Yes — for God's sake get a bath.' It brought a broad grin to the Patriarch's face.

The man then turned his attention to the Turk and the Austrian lady. They both gave him an affectionate look. He smiled back at them but said nothing.

The Patriarch withdrew a syringe from a hidden pocket and examined the contents of the serum closely. The man was up to his maximum intake with this dose, one milligram over and he could lose his mind altogether.

The Patriarch's hand shook slightly as if he were holding nitro-glycerine. The Austrian lady handed him a dab of cotton wool already coated with antiseptic. The man leant forward and bared his left arm. The Patriarch rubbed the antiseptic on to his arm and moved closer with the syringe. He didn't like using this method, but it was the only protection he could give him.

The man was taking a step into the dark. They didn't know who he would meet or what to expect. All they knew was that the next twenty four hours were going to be critical to their plans and the diabolical methods of interrogation used by the Reds if their suspicions were roused. They couldn't afford to take chances, they had waited too long.

The man sitting opposite the Patriarch was waiting his final course of treatment for his defence against any such interrogation. Already he had had twelve other injections. Already his subconscious had been deflated and pumped with all the facts and data of the man he was to impersonate. Already he was a paranoiac, ready to be pushed over the razors edge into the personality of the dead man. But they couldn't push him too far over the edge, or else he would become the dead man — he would become one of them and be lost forever. He had to become the dead man for a short while and still be on their side, without knowing anything that could give himself away. It was selected psychological mind-bending, a dangerous game to play either with friend or foe.

The Patriarch sighed, he was no Pavlov and the man sitting opposite was no dog. But it had to be done and he leant forward and injected the serum into the man's arm.

The man smiled and sat back in his seat. The Patriarch slowly swung the crucifix, which hung around his neck, from side to side. The man's eyes followed its movements until his pupils became dilated and his eyes glassy.

The Patriarch stopped his movements. Sitting opposite him in a hypnotic trance was not the man who had been sitting timidly in the corner seat by the window, but Dimitri Nickovitch, special agent of the Russian Secret Service. The injection had resurrected all the previous indoctrination.

The Patriarch leant forward to the man and spoke to him very quietly and gently in Russian.

'You are impersonating Dimitri Nickovitch. You must forget your real identity and remember only the facts that you have learned about Dimitri Nickovitch. You are not to try to remember who you really are, you know it will all come back to you very soon. You will only remember that you have taken a drug to enable you to forget your real identity for a short while. You are not to disclose who you really are or that you are only impersonating Nickovitch to anyone, no matter what pressure or pain may be inflicted upon you. Do you understand?'

The man opposite slowly nodded his head and said, 'I understand.'

'Good,' the Patriarch continued. 'You will remember all you have learned about Dimitri Nickovitch, so that you can now take his place. When you awake from your sleep, you will not remember who any of the occupants of this compartment are. You will not remember what has happened to the other Dimitri Nickovitch. You will only recall you boarded the train at Plovdiv and are to alight at the Romanian border, where you will be escorted to your destination. When you awaken you will go to the toilet at the end of the corridor, where you will mentally prepare yourself for your role.'

The Patriarch was well aware from the past that the first ten minutes was a time of great mental stress for the patient.

'Now, Dimitri,' he said cheerfully but equally softly, 'let us see how well you remember your lessons. Where were you born?'

'In the Ukraine.'

'What year?'

'1934.'

'What did they call your parents?'

'My mother was called Marfria and my father, Kuprik.'

'Have you any brothers or sisters?'

'No.'

'What happened to your mother and father?'

'My father was killed by the Germans when they invaded the country in 1940 and my mother died in the prison camp.' The man's voice trembled as he spoke, the memory was obviously painful to him.

'Where was the prison camp?'

'First we were in Vinnitsa and then we moved to Lasi in Romania.'

'When your mother died, who looked after you?'

'The Slevoskys.'

'How long did you live with them?'

'When we returned to the Ukraine after the war, I lived with them in Vinnitsa until I was eighteen.'

'Did they have any family?'

'Yes, two daughters, Anna and Tonya.'

'Were they younger than you?'

'Yes, Anna was one year younger and Tonya three years younger.'

'When did you last see them?'

'When I left Vinnitsa to go to University.'

'You did not like living in Vinnitsa?'

'No, they made fun of me in school because I was older than the rest.'

'Yes, that is correct Dimitri,' the Patriarch said gently, 'but you worked hard — you were determined to succeed. In 1950 you went to the University in Kharkov, where you studied languages. Then where did you go?'

'To Moscow, to work in the Department of Foreign Information.'

'Who was in charge of the Department?'

'Comrade Tomarovsky.'

'How long did you work there?'

'Until last year, when I was transferred to the KGB.'

'Where have you spent the last twelve months?'

'Near Moscow, at a special training school and at Spirov in Bulgaria.'

'And where are you travelling to?'

'To Plentita in Romania, where I am to be sent to a special training camp.'

'What is the purpose of this training?'

'To prepare me to go to England as a Soviet agent.'

'When did you first learn to speak English?'

'A lady in the prison camp taught me.'

'Who was she?'

'She was the camp doctor. I used to run errands for her.'

'What other languages did you learn to speak?'

'German, Romanian, Bulgarian.'

'You had a flair for languages?'

'Yes.'

The Patriarch paused, the man was responding well.

'When did you join the Communist Party?' he continued.

'In 1950, when I went to the university.'

'But you were already a member of the Young Communists before that?'

'Yes.'

The Patriarch changed his line of questions.

'I am going to mention some names, I want you to tell me who they are … Guishotin?'

'He was my Professor at University.'

'Bromovsky?'

'I share a room with him in Moscow. His is assistant director in the Department of Foreign Information.'

The train took a sharp bend and the man in the hypnotic trance slumped forward. The Patriarch quickly caught him and gently pushed him back. The Austrian lady gave the Patriarch a worried look, but the Patriarch quickly continued selecting names at random.

'Camelovsky?'

'He was in charge of my training in Moscow.'

'Timovitch? Mikolyn? Simderosty?'

'They were at the Moscow training school.'

'That will do,' the Patriarch said gently. 'Now, go to sleep. In ten minutes you will awaken. You will not remember who you are. You will only recall that you must impersonate Dimitri Nickovitch and that you have taken a drug which will eventually wear off. You must not let anyone learn that you are not the real Nickovitch, no matter what pain you may have to suffer. Do you understand — never?'

The man slowly nodded his head.

'Now sleep.'

The man leant back against his seat. Through a chink in the blind, the Patriarch could see the soldier leaning against the carriage window to steady himself. He looked uncomfortable and bored. The Patriarch clasped his hands and waited…

Chapter Three

Dimitri Nickovitch slowly opened his eyes. Foul smelling cigar smoke irritated his nostrils and he cursed the man in the corner for his inconsideration. He looked around the dimly-lit compartment. A large, portly looking Patriarch was sitting opposite him making rumbling noises in his long flowing beard. An elderly lady sat in the same seat as himself, patiently knitting. His eyes felt heavy and his head ached. He put his hand up to his face to rub his eyes and felt the weight of the briefcase which was attached to his wrist. Quickly he dropped his hand again and replaced his hat over his wrist. He looked at the man opposite and was thankful he had not been watching him.

He felt dazed and puzzled. What was he doing in this compartment? Why was he on this train? Where was he going? Why was the briefcase attached to his wrist? A wave of panic passed through his body as he tried to find the answers. *Steady Dimitri*, he said to himself, *steady, take it easy and sort it out calmly*.

Dimitri Nickovitch, Dimitri Nickovitch, he repeated the name mentally to himself over and over again. *I am Dimitri Nickovitch, a Soviet agent, travelling to Plentita in Romania. I boarded the train at Plovdiv.* He closed his eyes. His brain told him he had boarded the train at Plovdiv, but he couldn't picture himself doing it. His brain told him he was an agent of the KGB, the department that attended to the intelligence needs of the Soviet Government and that he had been systematically trained, indoctrinated and transferred around the Soviet Union into the Balkans, so that he would be forgotten by the world he once knew — but he couldn't get the picture. He knew the facts and the details, but not the pictures.

Again the panic gripped his body and perspiration appeared on his brow. What had happened to him? Why did he know the answers, but not remember the scenes?

Cautiously, he opened his eyes and slowly glanced around him. The other passengers were not watching him. A crucifix, hanging around the Patriarch's neck, held his attention — it appeared familiar. He dragged his eyes away. He was a Communist — a good Communist — he had no time for such symbols. But his eyes felt drawn to that piece of metal. The Patriarch shuffled in his seat and turned his body towards the window, so hiding the crucifix.

Again, Nickovitch tried to piece the jigsaw together. Why couldn't he picture the scenes? Why? Why? Why? — slowly, very slowly, from the dulled corners of his mind came the answer. He was not the real Dimitri Nickovitch, he was impersonating him. He had taken his place, he had assumed his identity. The knowledge brought him momentary relief.

Again, he opened his eyes to make certain he was not being observed, then a fresh wave of panic took hold of him. If he wasn't Nickovitch, who was he? Perspiration flowed from his brow as he mentally wrestled with the problem. *Who was he?* He felt trapped, the compartment seemed to have become smaller, the cigar smoke thicker. *Who was he?* He grabbed his briefcase and hat and stood up. He had to get out of the compartment, he had to get away from those three stupid mutes. He opened the compartment door and entered the corridor.

The soldier turned and looked at him with surprise.

'I thought you were sleeping, Comrade,' he said. He spoke Bulgarian and Nickovitch answered him in the same tongue.

'I was, but I want to go to the toilet.'

He didn't wait for an answer and worked his way along the narrow corridor. He passed the other crowded compartments without seeing them — he had to be alone. When he reached the small room he was thankful that it was not occupied. The soldier had followed him and he brusquely ordered him to wait outside. He entered the toilet and closed the door. The movement of the train made him hold on to the wash basin for support and for a while he remained in that position, studying his face in the small mirror.

Who am I? he asked himself desperately. His face looked unfamiliar, sallow and lean, with dark, sleek waved hair. His eyes were blue, but looked glassy as if he were drunk. His teeth were white and even. He touched his nose and felt his eyebrows, they were sore to the touch.

He gazed into the mirror. Why did his eyes look so dull? Had he been drugged? Something inside his brain clicked and the mechanism started again. He had been drugged. He had taken a drug so he would forget who he really was.

A calmness took over from the storm. He knew he was supposed to be Dimitri Nickovitch and now he knew he had been drugged so that he would forget all else. The drug would wear off in time and he would remember. He knew he was right and gave a long audible sigh. He remembered the soldier standing outside and flushed the toilet to forestall any suspicions. He pressed the tap of the wash basin and a dirty looking liquid was ejected into the basin. Again, he looked at his face, it still looked unfamiliar. He touched his eyebrows, they had been shaved.

From his personal features he turned his attention to his clothes. Underneath his heavy gabardine raincoat he was wearing a coarse, dark brown suit — the colour was not to his choosing. His shirt was of thick flannel material, fawn in colour and his tie a drab brown silk. He didn't admire Nickovitch's taste.

Quickly, he examined his pockets. Inside his raincoat pocket he found a packet of Russian cigarettes and a box of matches. His suit pockets were empty except the inside pocket of his jacket, in which he found a wallet. This contained his passport, a Soviet passport, his membership card to the Communist Party and a small amount of Russian and Bulgarian currency. In his trouser pockets was some loose currency and a handkerchief.

He studied the passport. It had only been issued a short while ago and was unmarked. Underneath his photograph his brief facts read: Profession — journalist. Place and date of Birth — Moscow, February 9th, 1932: Country of residence — Union of Soviet Socialist Republics: Height — 5' 11": Colour of eyes — blue: Colour of hair — black: Special peculiarities — scar on neck.

He replaced the contents back in his pocket and turned to leave the toilet. On a plaque on the wall were various notices about flushing the W.C. and the use of the paper towels. They were written in five different languages. He could read and understand them all, but for a moment he hesitated. Although he could read and understand the notices, he was mentally translating them all into one common language — and that language was English. He didn't know who he really was, but now he didn't want to remember. He knew sufficient to realise the dangerous part he was playing.

He opened the door, nodded to the soldier and returned to his seat in the compartment.

Chapter Four

It was approaching one a.m. when the train pulled into the small station on the border of Bulgaria and Romania. Without hesitation, Nickovitch left the train, accompanied by the soldier. He felt neither fear nor elation only grim determination to play his part.

From the station he was driven to the border control point where he was quickly transferred into another car and accompanied by an officer of the Romanian army, taken over the pass and into the valley below.

When the car eventually came to a halt it was outside an unpretentious-looking building with a large, iron studded door and high windows, in the corner of a village square.

Nickovitch followed the officer through an entrance porch into a brightly-lit foyer. The intense brightness hurt his eyes and it was a few seconds before his pupils adjusted themselves. They were standing in a large, rectangular-shaped entrance hall. At one end was a reception counter, but instead of room keys and hotel notices being displayed, the racks were filled with cigarettes and toilet requisites — it was being used as a shop. The walls were lined with dark, ornate, dirty wallpaper, the ceiling enriched with yellow mouldings and on the floor a threadbare red carpet.

They had been admitted into the building by a heavily-built man with short, black hair and heavy jowls. His left breast pocket bulged where he kept his armoury. He left them in the hallway and entered a side door. Nickovitch waited patiently. The officer who had escorted him stood silently by his side.

When the man returned, he was accompanied by a tall, thin, aristocratic-looking man, with straight grey hair and sharp, rather sinister, features. Despite the lateness of the hour, he was smartly dressed in a western style suit. He was smoking a black cigar from a small holder. With a movement of his hand he dismissed the officer. He motioned Nickovitch to follow him into a side room, not the one he had come out of, but another one which appeared to be his office.

'Your briefcase, Comrade Nickovitch,' he said. He spoke in Russian with a soft, cultured accent.

Nickovitch placed the briefcase on the table and the man unlocked the chain from the lock and from his wrist.

'Your passport, Comrade,' he said.

Nickovitch handed it over. The man didn't even give it a cursory glance, but handed the passport and the briefcase over to his assistant who had been standing behind Nickovitch and who immediately left the room with the documents.

'Sit down.' The man with the cigar indicated a seat. 'I am Colonel Reitzler.' It wasn't an introduction — it was a statement of fact. Nickovitch sat down and looked at the aristocratic face with the hard cold eyes. Up till now he had said nothing, but he didn't intend to stay dumb. He was a Soviet agent and a member of the Party. He was one of the communist elite.

'How long will I be here, Comrade?' he asked.

The man shrugged.

'One day — two days —' he said. 'It depends.' He didn't enlarge on what it depended upon. 'I trust you had a pleasant journey.'

'The compartment reeked of the foul odour of a Greek Patriarch and a Turkish capitalist,' Nickovitch snapped.

'That was unfortunate,' Reitzler agreed, 'but there are no landing strips near here and it is a long journey by road.'

'It could have been worse,' Nickovitch muttered.

The man who had taken the documents re-entered the room and handed over the passport to Reitzler.

'Here is your passport,' Reitzler said to Nickovitch. 'We shall attend to any further business in the morning. I have work to do.' He turned to his assistant. 'Show Comrade Nickovitch to his room and explain the arrangements.'

'Yes, Colonel,' the man muttered.

Reitzler left the room without further comment. Nickovitch watched him depart. He knew his type. A Colonel in the present Secret police of the Romanian Communist Party — had probably held the same rank and position in the previous regime. A Communist in name only. A ruthless inquisitor, allowed to retain his position by virtue of his knowledge of the Balkan underworld.

'This way, Colonel,' the other man said.

Nickovitch picked up his suitcase and followed the man out of the room and up a flight of stairs.

As they approached the first-floor landing, Nickovitch hesitated and glanced behind him. Standing in the hallway was the Colonel, watching him closely. Nickovitch held his gaze defiantly for a moment, then continued on his way up the stairs.

He was escorted along a narrow corridor. Halfway along, the man leading stopped, opened a door and switched on an electric light.

'This is your room, Comrade,' he said. 'Breakfast is at seven in the room next to the Colonel's office.'

Nickovitch entered the room and the man departed. It was more like a cell than a hotel bedroom. It only contained a single iron bed, a four legged table and a chair. There was no wash basin and the only feature which relieved the monotony of the dull green distempered walls was a small mirror. There was one small window glazed with heavy obscure glass fixed to the frame so that it couldn't be opened. Ventilation was provided by two iron grilles, one fixed to the external wall and the other to the corridor wall above the door.

Nickovitch lit a cigarette and studied the various fittings casually but carefully. The room would be bugged, of that he had no doubt, but it didn't bother him, he was not in the habit of talking in his sleep. What did concern him was in case he was being observed by way of a hidden close-circuit T.V. camera. The mirror was the obvious place, but it was fixed by four screws which appeared to be loose. There was a gap separating the mirror from the wall. The light fitting and the two vent grilles were the only other possibilities, but his trained eye could detect no indication of a camera.

Satisfied that he was not being observed, he opened his case and examined its contents. He was travelling light — a spare shirt, a change of underclothes, pair of socks, handkerchief, shaving equipment and a worn toothbrush. From the contents he turned his attention to the case itself, but it disclosed no secret compartment. He replaced the articles of clothing back in the case and started to undress. As he switched off the electric light he noticed the door to his room was not capable of being locked. A little apprehensive, he got into bed.

Nickovitch slept uneasily and awoke early. For a long while he lay on the bed, mentally sorting out his confused mind and reassuring himself. Presently, he dressed and made his way to a nearby bathroom.

Once or twice the door was rattled as someone tried to enter the room, but Nickovitch took his time. An alarm bell gave a sudden shrill ring and he glanced at his watch. It was seven a.m., time for breakfast.

He left the bathroom and made his way down the stairs without meeting anyone. The building had an uncanny silence about it like an empty museum. He opened the door of the room next to the Colonel's and entered the dining room. It was a long, narrow room, furnished like the rest of the building with heavy, old fashioned furniture, drab wallpaper and fading carpets. A long dining table occupied the centre of the room, whilst at one end were a number of easy chairs and small tables covered with magazines.

Sitting at the table eating their breakfast were four men. Two had their backs to him, but the other two were facing the door. One of the men facing him, a fair haired man in his middle twenties, gave him a quick nod of recognition and continued with his breakfast. The man next to him gave no such sign.

Nickovitch purposely took a seat facing the door, away from the fair haired man. One of the men who had previously had his back to him nodded his head, the man next to him just looked and turned away.

Nickovitch felt uncomfortable. He was at a disadvantage. Two of the men in the room knew him, but although he might know of them, he couldn't recognise them. This could prove fatal. He had to find out who they were before he made a slip. But how? Conversation appeared to be discouraged by the silence which accompanied the meal. It was just as well, he thought, it could also be dangerous.

A side door opened and an old man appeared, carrying a tray. He had a stooped gait and an impassive expression on his face. He placed a breakfast in front of Nickovitch and a pot of coffee. In silence, Nickovitch ate his breakfast, at the same time carefully studying the features of the other four men. The fair haired man was the youngest in appearance. The other man who had indicated he knew Nickovitch, was much older and had slightly greying, black hair. He appeared to be quite tall and of medium build.

The two other men were both middle aged men of medium stature. One thing they all had in common was a distinct lack of outstanding features. Of the four men, the fair haired one stood out due to his light colouring, but even his features were nondescript. They all had the type of faces that were difficult to describe. An everyday appearance that could fit any role. They could be passed over and not noticed. Their clothes, however, placed them, without doubt, on the eastern side of the iron curtain. Their dark, drab, serge suits and flannel shirts would never have seen daylight in even the cheapest tailor's shop in the west.

The continued silence was oppressive. It was like having breakfast in a dentist's waiting room. The door opened and as Nickovitch looked up, a woman entered. She hesitated at the door and looked around the room. She was dressed in a plain white blouse and black skirt. Her eyes fell on Nickovitch and there was a visible look of surprise. Nickovitch quickly turned his head away.

The door closed and when he looked up again the woman had gone. From the corner of his eye, he caught the fair haired man watching him. Feverishly, he wondered if he had made a mistake. Had his presence alarmed the woman? Who was she? Did he know her? But there was nothing he could do but wait. He had lost his appetite, but forced himself to eat the breakfast.

The man opposite Nickovitch, who had indicated he knew him, rubbed his hand across his stubbly chin and decided to have a shave. He stood up and left the room. Nickovitch waited a few seconds and then followed him. Somehow he had to find out who he was. It might help him to identify the other man and the woman.

He climbed the stairs and on the first floor landing stopped to light a cigarette. He fumbled in his pocket and stood in a position where he could observe the corridor leading to his bedroom. He saw the man appear from one of the bedrooms and he stood back so that he wouldn't be seen. The man was stripped to the waist and carried a towel. Nickovitch waited until he had entered the bathroom, then quickly walked along the corridor and entered the room the man had just vacated.

The room was similar to his own, but it wasn't the furniture he was interested in, it was the man's jacket. He saw it lying on the bed and hastily he felt in the pockets and took out the man's passport. Ivan Timovitch, he read. He placed it back in the jacket. Timovitch was one of the agents Nickovitch had trained with in Moscow. He turned to leave the room when the door opened and Timovitch entered.

Nickovitch's brain worked overtime.

'Hello, Ivan,' he said casually.

Timovitch's face reflected both surprise and anger, but without comment he brushed roughly past Nickovitch and collected a bar of soap from his case. He left the room and waited for Nickovitch to join him in the corridor.

'What the devil do you want, Nickovitch?' Timovitch demanded furiously in a subdued tone.

'Don't get alarmed, Comrade,' Nickovitch said calmly. 'I only wanted to ask you if I could borrow your toothpaste. I appear to have left mine behind.'

Timovitch looked at him suspiciously. 'Get it downstairs,' he snarled and disappeared into the bathroom.

Nickovitch sighed. He had managed to bluff his way out of a nasty spot, but the microphone could still have picked up their voices. He consoled himself with the knowledge he had gained. Timovitch had been one of four men who had trained together in Moscow — Timovitch, Mikolyn, Simderosty and Nickovitch. The fair haired man could well be Mikolyn or Simderosty, but he couldn't be certain.

He had to continue with his pretence and he quickly descended the staircase again. At the rear of the reception counter were a variety of toilet requisites and cigarettes. He took a tube of toothpaste and a packet of cigarettes, the same brand he had in his pocket and returned to his bedroom.

He had no sooner entered his room, however, when there was a knock on his door. He opened the door and came face to face with the woman who had appeared in the breakfast room downstairs.

'Hullo, Dimitri,' she said, 'have I changed so much in eight years that you didn't recognise me?' Her tone was sharp, cryptic, reflecting no emotion, but her dark eyes watched his reactions critically.

Eight years, that would be the time he was supposed to have been at university. My God! he thought, she could be one of thousands.

'Hullo, Comrade,' he said, playing for time, 'the lighting was so poor downstairs…'

It was a lame excuse.

She came into the room uninvited. Feverishly, Nickovitch searched for a way to make amends for his oversight.

'You haven't really changed very much,' he said calmly, 'now that I can get a good look at you, but eight years in a long time.'

'I often wondered if our paths would cross again, Dimitri,' she said. Her accent was that of the South, from the area Nickovitch was supposed to have come from. Again, her tone gave no indication of how she felt about meeting him. He studied her face in a vain attempt he would get some clue that would help him. Her face was not pretty, but also not unattractive, with dark brown eyes and dark hair. But like her tone, it showed no genuine emotion. She looked hard, cold, like a well-trained Party disciple.

'This is not the place I would have expected to meet you, Comrade,' Nickovitch said.

She frowned. 'Isn't it, Dimitri?' she said. 'It is not really so surprising when you consider our careers have followed similar channels.'

Nickovitch lit another cigarette. What did she mean — similar channels? Had she also worked in the Department of Foreign Information?

'You never wrote when you left university,' she remarked.

'I was so busy in Moscow,' he replied, 'and my work was such...' He shrugged his shoulders.

'I understand,' she said coolly. 'Did you know that father had died?'

'No, I did not,' he said with feeling. 'I am sorry.'

'Are you?' she asked icily.

Nickovitch ignored her question. He was getting nowhere. With every remark he could be putting a noose tight around his neck. He had to play a long shot.

'How are the rest?' he asked.

'Anna has four children now,' she said.

Anna, Anna. He walked over and sat on the bed as he mentally juggled with the name. The only Anna he knew was

Anna Sklevosky, daughter of Andre Sklevosky, the family with whom Nickovitch had lived with when his mother died.

My God, he thought, is that who she means? Anna Sklevosky? Was that why she was telling him about her father? And her accent was that of the Ukraine. His pulse quickened. She must be Tonya! Tonya Sklevosky. No wonder she was surprised when he hadn't recognised her. But he had to be absolutely certain. If he gave her the wrong identity, he would be committing suicide.

'Anna will be very pleased,' he said and added cautiously, 'where is she living now?'

'In Vinnitsa, of course, in the old house,' she replied irritably.

It confirmed his suspicions, this was Tonya — Tonya Sklevosky, with whom Nickovitch had lived, both in the prison camp and later in Vinnitsa. She knew Nickovitch like a brother. She could catch him out with a thousand and one questions. He had to change the subject before he made a slip.

'Well,' he said, 'perhaps our paths will cross again.' He resisted the temptation to call her by her name. He could still be wrong. 'I hope so,' he added.

'Do you?' she asked. 'You never have before.'

Nickovitch inwardly cursed. He wasn't responding the way the real Nickovitch would have done. He sensed it. He also sensed she didn't like him, she despised him. Not that her feelings unduly worried him, what he feared more was did she suspect him? Would she report him? The thought of having to answer to the Colonel reminded him of the hidden microphone and he decided to get in some propaganda.

'We must forget the past,' he said solemnly, 'and concentrate on our work — for the sake of the Party.'

Tonya flushed up and looked at him scornfully.

'You don't have to tell me my duty,' she snapped. 'I know it very well.' She abruptly turned and left the room.

Nickovitch remained seated on the bed, mentally exhausted. He could not have had a more dangerous interview, he could not have picked a more capable interrogator. He went over the conversation which had taken place. On balance, he reckoned, he hadn't fared too badly, but then he thought of Tonya's hard, cold features and wasn't too sure. She must also be a trained Soviet agent, otherwise she wouldn't be here and as such, a very clever and astute woman. It was incredible that she of all people, should be in the same building hidden away in the Balkans. Incredible even if he had been the real Nickovitch. There had to be a reason why the spymasters in the Kremlin had brought them together. It was no accident.

He felt things were coming apart at the seams. If she was as clever as he suspected, then she would be suspicious and when a good Communist is suspicious, they report it immediately. It was part of their way of life, it was their form of confession. He decided to remain where he was — it reduced the risk of any further clashes with other Soviet agents.

Nickovitch was summoned shortly after ten o'clock by the man who had shown him to his room the previous evening. He was taken to the room the Colonel had appeared from when Nickovitch had been standing in the hallway. It was a large room, lit by electric light — there were no windows. Surrounding the room were metal filing cabinets and desks. At one end was a dentists' chair.

Standing waiting for him was a small bespectacled man in a white coat with a stethoscope hanging round his neck.

'Take off your clothes,' the doctor ordered, his beady eyes studying Nickovitch closely.

Nickovitch stripped off and the doctor set about examining his body with meticulous care. Nothing was overlooked, even his fingerprints and blood group were checked. It was something bigger than a normal medical. It was obvious they were suspicious of him.

The doctor had a rough and clumsy manner and when he came to examine Nickovitch's teeth he poked about in his mouth until he dislodged a small filling. With an almost sadistic delight, he set about making good the damage. Nickovitch was furious, but withheld his anger. When he eventually left the room, however, his jaw was still aching.

The man who had escorted him there was waiting in the hallway.

'The Colonel wants to see you,' he said gruffly.

Nickovitch entered the Colonel's room. He was sitting at his desk, his long fingers playing with a pencil.

'Sit down, Comrade Nickovitch,' he said. His tone was neither patronising nor threatening.

'I wish to make a complaint,' Nickovitch said hotly, 'about that butcher across there.' He pointed to the room he had just left.

'Sit down,' the Colonel ordered abruptly.

Nickovitch sat down and glowered.

'What were you doing in Timovitch's room?' the Colonel asked quietly, his eyes watching every movement of Nickovitch's face.

'I went to borrow his toothpaste,' Nickovitch replied evenly. 'I didn't have any.'

The Colonel gave him a mocking, disbelieving look.

'You did not recognise Comrade Sklevosky when she entered the dining room this morning,' he said, changing the subject.

'Who told you that?' Nickovitch demanded, knowing quite well where he got his information from. 'I recognised Comrade Sklevosky all right.'

The Colonel raised his eyebrows. 'She did not think so.'

'I do not care what she thinks,' Nickovitch said hotly. 'I recognised her, but I did not think it was wise to show it in the dining-room. It was one of the rules I was taught in Moscow.'

'You were also taught not to go into anyone else's room, Comrade.'

'That was for some toothpaste.'

'Toothpaste?'

'Yes, Comrade, toothpaste.' Nickovitch stood up and leant on the table. 'I demand to know what this is all about. First that butcher across the passage and now these questions. I assure you I am well thought of in Moscow.'

'This is not Moscow, Comrade.'

Nickovitch glowered at the man, but the Colonel held his gaze with his sinister eyes.

'You can go, Comrade,' he said softly. 'There is nothing further for the present.'

It sounded like a warning.

Nickovitch stormed out of the room and returned to his bedroom. He lit a cigarette and lay on the bed. What did he mean — for the present? Was he in for further interrogation? He cursed Tonya and he cursed his damnable bad luck.

With a feeling of foreboding, Nickovitch waited for his next summons. At noon the bell rang indicating the midday meal. Nickovitch went to the dining room and was surprised to see he was the only one present. Again the old man with the stooped gait served him his meal.

When he had finished, Nickovitch remained in the room and read the various Communist propaganda magazines that lay scattered around the small tables which represented the hotel lounge. The room was oppressive, sombre and dirty. The building was deadly silent.

Nickovitch could have been the only one there, but he knew he wasn't. He knew he was being watched — his every movement being reported to the Colonel. He knew their technique — keeping him in solitary suspense was part of their plan. From the dining room he eventually returned again to his bedroom and lay on the bed.

In the evening the bell rang again. The last thing he felt like was food, but he knew it would be unwise to pass it over. He descended the stairs and entered the dimly-lit dining room. The meal that was served was badly cooked and foul tasting. He gladly accepted the coffee that was brought to him.

He drank the coffee, but as he replaced the cup on its saucer realised, only too late, that he had been drugged. His head swam and his vision became blurred. He felt himself losing control of his limbs. He struggled to his feet, but sank to the floor unconscious.

Chapter Five

In the dark abyss of his mind he saw a fiery ball approach him. It came close up to him and moved away. Again it approached him, closer … closer… Mentally he tried to move his hands to his face, but nothing happened. He couldn't stop it getting closer … closer…

He yelled as a seething, burning pain tore through his body. The pain was unbearable, he had to get away from it … he had to … he felt himself screaming … screaming … and then peace — darkness. From the pit of his unconscious came a question — *who are you? Who are you?*

Again the ball of fire whirled in front of him. He had to stop it before it engulfed him again — but he couldn't move — the agonising pain twisted and ripped into his body. He yelled, screamed and all of a sudden it was peace again… *Who are you? Who are you?*

He had a vision of a small white house surrounded with olive trees… *Who are you? Who are you?* The vision vanished. He was standing alone in darkness… A needle like a ray of light appeared in front of him and he felt a torturous, stabbing pain… It got worse … worse … he couldn't move … it got worse … worse … again he yelled … again the darkness.

Who are you? Who are you? He saw a shrivelled-up little body all twisted and groaning — it was his body! Another sharp needle like jab… He screamed as the body twisted in agony … the jabs were longer, tearing at his soul … he was fumbling for words … screaming a name … screaming … screaming.

Nickovitch moved his head, it was on something soft, but it ached, hammered, throbbed. He tried to move his hands — they were free. He pressed them around his head to try to stop the throbbing. A nauseating wave of sickness engulfed his body and he writhed in agony. He tried to open his eyes, but the pain was too great.

Slowly, very slowly, he released his hands from his head and felt about him. He was on a bed. He half opened his eyes and saw the green walls of his bedroom. 'Thank God,' he muttered and sank back against his pillow. The pit of his stomach rebelled and he vomited uncontrollably over the side of the bed. He retched and twisted until it became an unconscious movement.

He lay back on the bed and groaned. Who am I? — Who am I? — Again he groaned, but now he knew who he was. The locked door in his mind had been opened. Now he knew he wasn't Dimitri Nickovitch, but Stephen Fletcher, a British subject, destined from birth to become one of their secret agents.

He closed his eyes and saw again the white-washed house surrounded by green olive trees where he had spent his youth. Who was it who had decided his destiny? he wondered. It couldn't have been his mother — she was too gentle, too sweet — it must have been his father. Again, he groaned, as the pain hammered at his head. Yes, he thought, it would be his father. He managed to turn on his back and gave a long, deep sigh. He knew who he was all right, the drug had worn off. He was one of those band of men, unheard of in Britain, who spent their lifetime serving their country hidden away in some foreign land. He was a name in a civil servant's dusty file, he was a name on an overseas account of a London bank. An account which mysteriously increased in size.

Yes, it would have been his father who had decided his destiny. His father who had also given a lifetime of service in the consulates of the Balkan countries. His father who had married the daughter of a Greek minister of state. Had that also been for the service of his country? he wondered.

He could see clearly how the die had been cast. Born in Greece where he had lived until he was four years old. From four until he was seven living in Hungary, then the war years in Turkey and after Turkey it had been Sofia in Bulgaria, then Romania and finally back to Greece. And all the time mixing and living with the local children, learning their language, their habits and their way of life.

At five, he had been bilingual, at twelve, he could speak three languages and at eighteen, five languages. There had been no Oxford education for him, that had not been part of his destiny. Instead, he had been sent to Ankara to study Russian. But then, at eighteen, he had been put on the payroll. He had been enrolled early in life in case they lost him. And, after Ankara, a life of wandering, seeing, learning — spying. And the country he served was only a place on the map — a place he had only visited once in his whole life, when his father had taken him on a short visit to meet his masters.

He groaned and twisted his body in an endeavour to get relief from the pain. He was not the storybook type of spy. Not the glamourized, tough playboy who could take punishment without suffering. He was real flesh and blood and at the moment he cared as little for the country he served as he did for his enemies.

He opened his eyes fully and took stock of his position. It was daylight. He looked at his watch — it was after six a.m. He had either been unconscious or asleep for nearly ten hours.

What had he said? What had he told them? His head ached as he tried to remember — it was hopeless. But he was back in his bedroom, that gave him hope. If he had confessed they would surely not have brought him back here. He couldn't have told them anything because at the time he didn't know, his mind had been shut off from his own past. No, he felt certain he had told them nothing.

They had prepared for such an emergency. The months of planning, the weeks of brainwashing, the mind-bending, had served him well. The Reds had tried too soon. If they had only waited a further ten hours he would have told them. He would have told them that the message had come from the very top — the Reds were getting hold of too much top level information — infiltrate — find the leaks and plug the gaps.

He would have told them of how the photograph of Nickovitch had been channelled via road, rail and mule, to their headquarters on the Greek island of Skiros. At their excitement when they had noticed the similarity with Fletcher. How they had set to work to build up a complete picture of Nickovitch so Fletcher could take his place. How he had spent months alone in the mountains on the Turkish-Russian border, patiently passing and receiving information via the wandering tribes who moved to and fro between the two countries.

He would have told them of their contacts in Moscow, even in the spy school itself, of his plastic surgery operations, of the hours, days, weeks, months they had spent planning and studying Nickovitch and embedding the facts in the subconscious of Fletcher's mind.

He would have told them how they were planning to send Fletcher into the Soviet Union itself, when the news had reached them that Nickovitch was being sent to Bulgaria and Romania for his final training. How they had prepared a plan for every mode of travel Nickovitch had adopted to get to the Romanian border. How they had bribed the railway car attendant and how the Turkish police had helped them with their plans. But they had been ten hours too soon and they had learned nothing.

He recalled the butcher of a dentist and the medical inspection the previous day. They would have learned nothing from that neither, he thought. Nickovitch's personal documents had been brought into line with Fletcher's details.

He heard people moving about the corridor. He was not alone any longer — another draft had arrived in transit. The bell sounded for breakfast, but he remained on the bed, helpless. Eventually he struggled to his feet, but his legs trembled under his weight. Footsteps approached his room and he held on to the bed and waited…

The door opened and the old man who served the meals entered the room. Without acknowledging Fletcher's presence, he placed a glass of water and two white pills on the table and departed. Was this an act of human kindness on the old man's part? Fletcher wondered. Was it a trick? Or was it because he had finally been accepted by them? Whatever the reason he took the pills and returned to his bed.

Gradually, the stimulants took effect and the wretched feeling passed. He went to the bathroom, washed and shaved and returned to his room again. He decided against going to the dining room in case he was recognised by other former colleagues of Nickovitch. Instead, he lit a cigarette to kill the stench from his vomit and allowed his body to fully recover from the harsh treatment it had received the previous evening.

Chapter Six

'You will go with Comrade Smith; he will take you to his training establishment... He is an Englishman.'

Fletcher sat poker-faced, listening to the Colonel's briefing. He had waited patiently to be called, not knowing what his fate was to be, but the Colonel's remarks settled the matter. He had been accepted, he was one of them again. No reference had been made to the previous evening by either party.

Fletcher realised the futility of complaining. It would only bring a blank denial or some fatuous remark about his sleeping habits. It would serve little purpose to cause any further irritation to Colonel Reitzler — but Fletcher would not forget — his time would come.

'You will remain with Smith until you receive your instructions from Moscow.'

'How long with that be?' Fletcher asked.

The Colonel shrugged. 'When Moscow are satisfied.'

'I understand.'

The Colonel leant forward and pressed a button on his desk.

'My suitcase is still in my room,' Fletcher explained.

'Leave it there,' the Colonel said.

'My papers?' Fletcher asked.

'You won't be needing them again,' the Colonel replied dryly.

The door opened and a man entered. Even before any introductions were made, Fletcher realised he was the Englishman the Colonel had referred to. In his hacking tweed jacket, cavalry trousers, suede shoes and high-necked pullover and cravat, he could have stepped out of any golf club, village pub or point to point meeting.

'This is Comrade Nickovitch, Comrade Smith,' the Colonel said, without moving from his seat, and to Fletcher he said, 'Comrade Smith.'

Fletcher stood up as Smith bounced over, hand outstretched. He was of the same height as Fletcher and slimly built. A man in his middle forties with a fresh open face, bright cheery eyes with a neat moustache and thinning hair.

They shook hands stiffly — Smith had a firm grip. There followed a delicate silence until Smith spoke.

'Well, Colonel,' he said breezily, his eyes flashing nervously from Fletcher to the Colonel, 'if you have nothing further, we will be on our way. I would like to get back for lunch.'

Colonel Reitzler shrugged. 'As you wish,' he said.

Smith gave a half laugh.

'Well, you know what these women are like. They don't like their meals spoilt.'

The Colonel gave him a contemptuous scowl and with a gesture of his hand, indicated they could leave.

Once outside the building, Smith paused and looked around him. Fletcher stood beside him, puzzled by his nervous manner. He had an air of guilt about him, as if he felt as much out of place as he looked.

The village square was surrounded by dirty yellow buildings. There were a number of people about, swarthy country people in their drab clothes. Parked in the square were four cars, but it was not difficult to pick out Smith's. It was a fawn British car with a British registration number and G.B. plates.

Smith walked over to it and Fletcher followed. Lying casually on the rear seat was a road map and two British daily newspapers. Smith could have been a British tourist straight from the channel ferry — only tourists were not allowed within a hundred miles of the area.

'Get in,' Smith said lightly. Fletcher felt disappointed, he had half expected him to say 'old boy'.

Fletcher took his place beside Smith and relaxed in the well upholstered seat.

'Nice car,' he said in Russian.

'If you don't mind, Comrade, you will speak only English now. It is part of your training.' Smith smiled as he spoke, an automatic, bland, disarming smile. But he added: 'Yes, it is a nice car, I have only had it since Christmas.'

So he understands Russian, Fletcher thought. He had a feeling there would be many more surprises if he was to get to know the real Smith. For instance, the car had right hand drive, not like the Continental cars. Where had he purchased it? — in England? Had he driven it down himself, or had it been shipped elsewhere? There were a lot of questions he would have liked to ask, but instead he asked: 'What make is it?'

'A Rover three litre,' Smith replied. 'Runs very well.'

He switched on the ignition and drove out of the square.

From the village they motored west, deep into the heart of the mountains. As the kilometres mounted up the nervousness Smith had displayed with Colonel Reitzler left him and in its place came the confident, beguiling manner of an experienced and entertaining host.

After they had been travelling for over an hour, Smith turned off the road onto a track which led to a dense forest which skirted the foothills and they drove past an armed lookout post, through the forest and came to a basin shaped valley about a mile across.

'This is my training camp,' Smith said with pride.

In the valley Fletcher saw a small Balkan village. Set aside from the village was a ranch type bungalow and a row of chalets. Beyond the village, on the edge of the forest, was a large hangar. They drove into the valley and up to the bungalow. As they got out of the car a woman appeared.

Like Smith, Fletcher placed her on the wrong side of forty. Her figure was losing the battle of the bulge and beginning to spread. Her face was heavily made up to disguise any sign of age and her hair was tinted at the edges to cover up her grey streaks. She was smartly dressed, however, in a two piece costume, but over decorated with jewellery.

'Comrade Nickovitch,' Smith said, 'this is my wife. Madge, this is Comrade Nickovitch.'

'How do you do Comrade… Oh dear, these names,' she said apologetically, 'I am afraid I do have difficulty with them.'

'Nickovitch,' Fletcher said, 'but it does not matter.'

'Do come in, anyway,' she said, her hand nervously touching her hair.

She ushered him into the bungalow as if he were a friend joining them for a holiday. The hall was just what he would have imagined a typical English country home to be like, with oak beamed ceiling, panelled walls, parquet flooring and numerous copper ornaments. Even an English style telephone standing on a small oak table.

'Now Charles, you take Comrade…' She didn't bother to try to remember his name, 'in for a drink while I see to the lunch.'

The casualness, the familiarity, the friendliness, amazed Fletcher. They could have been in Surrey, Yorkshire — anywhere rather than the heart of Romania.

'In here, Nickovitch,' Smith said. He opened a door leading off the hall and stood aside to let Fletcher enter the room.

Fletcher walked into the lounge and stopped dead in his tracks. Three other guests were also in the room. Three other agents whom he had met in transit the previous day. Ivan Timovitch, the fair haired man and Tonya Sklevosky.

He cursed himself for allowing the Smiths to lull him off his guard. This was not a visit to friends or relatives, nor a hotel guest house. This was a training school for Soviet agents. A very clever set up, run by two very clever people.

'You know each other,' Smith said lightly.

'Yes,' Fletcher replied.

Timovitch had stood up. 'You appeared to be surprised to see us,' he said.

Fletcher quickly replied, 'Not surprised to see you, Comrade Timovitch, but surprised to see you dressed so differently.'

'There are many things which are different here, Comrade,' Timovitch said.

Fletcher felt easier, he had covered up well. Their clothes were different and he knew why. They were dressed in western style garments. Timovitch was wearing a rather cheap-looking navy blue gabardine suit with waistcoat, more working-class in appearance. The fair haired man was in a more sporting attire, with a woollen sports shirt, thick, checked sports coat and light fawn flannels.

Tonya Sklevosky presented the greatest contrast to her previous austere appearance. She was wearing a colourful woollen dress with a pink cardigan loosely hanging over her shoulders, a pair of high heeled court shoes and fully fashioned stockings. Of the three, she appeared the most awkward and uncomfortable in her new style clothes. She sat stiff-backed on the edge of a settee, her face expressionless as before.

'You were right to stand up when we entered, Comrade Timovitch. You should have done so also, Comrade Mikolyn,' Smith said.

The names had not been missed by Fletcher. Unwittingly, Smith had confirmed Fletcher's suspicions about the fair haired man. He had supplied him with the one piece of information which could have proved his downfall. Fletcher felt more relaxed.

'Now, Comrade Sklevosky,' Smith carried on with his instructing, 'if you were the hostess, you would get the drinks. I think Comrade Nickovitch and I would like a gin and tonic.'

'Yes, Comrade Smith,' Tonya said stiffly. She stood up and walked over to a cocktail cabinet.

Fletcher glanced casually around the room. It was a large lounge and as he had now come to expect, typically British in its decoration and furnishings. Again the ceiling beams and parquet floor with loose rugs and a flower covered three piece suite and occasional chairs.

Tonya handed Smith and Fletcher their drinks.

Fletcher sipped his and purposely twisted his mouth as he pretended not to like the taste.

'You will have to get used to it,' Smith said. 'It is a popular drink at social functions.' He turned to the others who also had drinks in their hands.

'Tell me what you have been doing this morning, Comrade Timovitch,' he said.

Timovitch placed his drink on the table. 'First I read the newspapers, Comrade Smith, then I walked down to the English village and spent the morning studying the Labour Exchange and Post Office with Comrade Milne.'

Fletched noticed a cockney slant to Timovitch's accent — was this intentional? he wondered and who was Comrade Milne?

'And you, Comrade Mikolyn?' Smith asked.

Mikolyn spoke for the first time. His accent was not English and Fletcher immediately recognised the Australian drawl.

'Like Comrade Timovitch,' he said, 'I studied the newspapers and then went to the English village where I spent the morning in the bank and the public house.'

Smith turned to Tonya.

'What have you been doing, Comrade?' he asked.

'I have been with your wife all morning,' she replied. Her English was perfect, without trace of accent. 'We inspected the house, gave the cook and maid their instructions and then went down to the English village to shop.'

Fletcher listened attentively. It was obvious that they had a model English village somewhere, probably in the hangar. This didn't surprise him, but the presence of another Englishman made him curious.

He was surprised to see Smith turn to him.

'Well, Comrade Nickovitch,' Smith said, his eyes flashing, 'you have noticed their changes in clothes, you have heard them all speak in English. How would you place them if you came across them in England?'

Fletcher purposely waited before replying. He had to give a good appreciation without being too clever.

'Comrade Timovitch,' he said slowly picking his words carefully, 'spoke with a slight cockney accent. He is dressed in a rather cheap type of western suit. I should put him as one of the working-class, probably upper working-class — a post office worker — railway clerk — that type.'

'Good,' Smith said, 'go on.'

Fletcher turned his attention to Tonya. She sat, stone-faced, watching him.

'Comrade Sklevosky spoke without any trace of accent. Her clothes look fashionable. She could be the wife of a company director, or a doctor, or other professional man. Alternatively, she could be a career woman, herself.'

'Very good, very good,' Smith said eagerly.

'Comrade Mikolyn puzzles me,' Fletcher said. Mikolyn half smiled as if he were pleased at Fletcher's failure to place him. 'His accent is not one I can readily recognise. He has western style clothes, but they do not look English.' He shrugged. 'I am afraid I do not know.'

'You are correct in thinking he is not English,' Smith said. 'Tell Comrade Nickovitch where you come from.'

'Sydney, Australia,' Mikolyn drawled.

'Ah,' Fletcher said. 'Now I understand.'

'You did very well. Timovitch and Sklevosky are more or less what you thought. They are…' Smith stopped speaking. His wife had entered the room. 'Lunch ready, my dear?' he asked.

'Yes, Charles. Will you all come through to the dining room.' She smiled at them. They stood up and walked to the door.

In the dining room they sat at a long table with the Smiths at the heads, directing operations in their friendly, deluding manner. Fletcher sat opposite Tonya, but the only time any of the four students spoke was when asked a question.

The layout of the table was explained by Smith and the various etiquettes of having a meal. Timovitch being working-class and Mikolyn an Australian, were not expected to observe the same standards at the table as Nickovitch and Sklevosky. This was the first indication Fletcher had been given as to his intended role, but he made no comment — he was prepared to wait. The novelty of his surroundings had worn off the moment he had entered the lounge and he was constantly on his guard. He couldn't afford to display any further knowledge than the rest and he took his lead from them.

The meal was served by a maid, a girl in her early twenties dressed in a simple black dress and white apron. She spoke English, but her skin was darkly tanned. She was the first flaw in the stage design, she was a Balkan, probably Romanian. She wasn't part of the instructing staff, she was one of the stage hands necessary for the Smiths to act their part. She carried out her duties quickly and effectively and whenever she was in the room conversation stopped.

At the close of the meal, after the coffee had been served, Smith leant back in his chair, his arms on the rests and surveyed his class like a benevolent employer after a staff luncheon. Mrs Smith apparently knew the sign.

'If you are going to talk business, dear,' she said, 'I will go and see to the servants.'

She left the room and the class to her husband.

'Now that we are all here,' Smith said, 'I will explain the identities you are to assume and the course we will adopt.'

Fletcher brought out a packet of cigarettes, but Smith quickly handed him an English branded packet.

'The first thing you must all do is to forget that you are citizens of the Soviet Union. You must act and think in the roles I am going to give you. At no time, not even in your chalets, will you speak Russian, nor will you address each other as Comrade. Is that understood?'

They all nodded their heads. Smith, whose eyes quickly darted from one to another, continued: 'Timovitch, you are to be a Mister Henry Jackson, a Londoner by birth and a chauffeur by occupation. You have no family and your wife has recently died. This has considerably distressed you and will explain why you are moving into a boarding house. You have left your last employer and are awaiting for an application you have submitted to become a chauffeur, employed by the Government, to drive one of their official cars.

'Mikolyn, you are Gary Vincent, an Australian civil engineer. You qualified two years ago and decided to visit the old country. You are single, with an eye for the girls and intent on enjoying yourself. When you arrive in London, you will become employed by a firm of civil engineers. You will mix with the Commonwealth set and establish yourself amongst them.'

Smith turned his attention to Fletcher. 'Nickovitch, you are to be a Paul Adams, a man of considerable wealth, with a small export and import business. Your business is already established and you merely act as an agent, getting orders from abroad and passing them on to firms in Britain. It is a small concern which you maintain as an interest. Your parents are both dead and have left you a considerable inheritance and you frequently invest on the Stock Exchange. You have recently sold your house in North London and are renting a furnished detached house in Surrey. You have no family, but are married — Sklevosky, you are to be Mrs Jane Adams.'

He paused to see whether his last remark brought any reaction, any sign from Fletcher or Tonya, but Fletcher had also been well trained to show no outward emotion. Although he realised the full implications and dangers, he reflected none of his fears on his face. Similarly, Tonya had indicated no reaction — none of them had. They all sat silently, waiting for Smith to carry on with his briefing.

'You have been married for seven years, but have no children, although you would welcome a family. Mrs Adams, you help your husband with his business, you act as his secretary.'

Again Smith paused and surveyed the four agents.

'Jackson is to be the leader of the cell, he alone will give the orders, he alone will have contact with control. Jackson will arrange any meetings and you will obey his orders implicitly. Now that is the framework from which we will start. Each week you will receive more information about your roles until you have a full picture. Today is Tuesday, our next discussion on the subject will be on Friday, that gives you plenty of time to consider the problems. Any questions?'

No one spoke. Fletcher was out on a limb with Tonya. They were to have no contact with control or Moscow. He didn't like it at all. He was risking his neck impersonating Nickovitch and he was ending up in a London suburb. But, like the rest, he knew better than to question any instructions laid down by Moscow.

'You will all report here at eight a.m. each morning for breakfast,' Smith continued. 'In the mornings you will receive instructions in the English village. After lunch, you will be given lectures by myself or my wife, or Mr Milne. We will also have film shows. In the evenings you will watch television — you will learn a lot from it. Finally, we shall round the evening off with a discussion and questions on your day's work. It will be a long day, but you have a lot to learn and we have not much time.

'Now, this afternoon I want to take Adams to the village to get his wardrobe sorted out and meet Milne. Mrs Adams, you will remain with my wife, who has a programme arranged for you. Jackson, your local football team, Chelsea, are playing a match this afternoon. It is on television, you will watch the game and learn all the names of the players. When it is over, you will go to the library in the village and study the progress of your team during the past season.

'Vincent, you probably have the easier role, as you won't be expected to know too much about the English scene. I think you had better spend the afternoon in the library, refreshing yourself about Australia. We shall meet here again at six, for our evening viewing.'

Smith sat back in his chair, again the friendly host.

Fletcher admired their thoroughness. English tutors in an English home and an English village equipped with library, bank, etc. Taped English television programmes, probably only a few days old. Nothing had been left to chance.

Arrangements were even being made to receive them in London. An export business, an application for a job — he had to hand it to them. And the agents themselves, he didn't doubt had been also thoroughly trained. Timovitch, the working-class chauffer could probably drive any make of car he would come across, — he would know the geography of London better than any Londoner himself.

Vincent, the civil engineer — he most likely topped the lists in the Moscow University department of Engineering. He felt uneasy about his own role, export and import was something he knew little about and living with Tonya could prove dangerous. She knew too much about Nickovitch, more than Fletcher knew himself. That was why Moscow had trained her for the role — that was why their paths had crossed again after eight years apart. Moscow had thought of everything, but to Fletcher, she was the big fly in the ointment.

Smith stood up.

'We meet again at six,' he said. 'Adams, I will join you on the veranda in a few moments.'

When Smith appeared on the veranda, Fletcher was surprised to see a Great Dane trailing at his feet. Smith completed the picture of an Englishman taking his dog for a stroll by collecting a walking stick from a stand and like a man showing off his estate, he escorted Fletcher over to the hangar, on the way pointing out the chalet Fletcher was to use and other various buildings.

Inside the hangar was not a model village, as Fletcher had expected, but a full-size replica of a high street of a suburban town. It was a masterpiece of imitation made from plywood and cardboard, except for a few essential fittings. Its effect was most realistic.

Smith's assistant, Milne, was also not as expected. He was a small man with bushy eyebrows and straggling grey wisps of hair over his bald head. He had a friendly face with a constant benign smile and an almost servile manner. In the days that followed Fletcher saw a lot of Milne and his manner never changed and he was never seen anywhere, other than the hangar.

After the introductions had been made Fletcher was taken to a tailor's shop where Smith and Milne set about preparing his wardrobe. They also discarded his rough serge suit and re-dressed him in expensive western clothes. Like two artists they discussed and changed his attire until they were satisfied. When they had finished, however, gone was the dowdy Nickovitch and in his place stood, Paul Adams, successful businessman.

When Fletcher eventually left the hangar it was approaching five o'clock. Smith had some business to attend to with Milne and Fletcher strolled back to his chalet deep in thought. The set-up was well organised and long established. How many agents had passed though the school? he wondered and how many were now operating in England? Did London know such a place existed? Did they know about the Smiths and Milne? He was learning a lot, he had to make certain he was still alive at the end of it all, to be able to tell them about it.

He was still preoccupied with his thoughts as he entered his chalet. The chalet, he found, was roomy and pleasantly furnished with fitted carpet, pair of divan beds, side tables, dressing table and wardrobe. It was an improvement on his previous bedroom.

He glanced at the beds, on one of them lay a pink cardigan — Tonya's cardigan. Puzzled, he walked over to the dressing table and opened a drawer. Inside was a variety of cosmetics. Had Smith made a mistake? Was this Tonya's room? He turned his attention to the wardrobe and found not only a number of dresses, but also several suits. Instantly he realised their significance. Smith had certainly not made a mistake. This was the room he was to share with Tonya. This was where he was starting his married life.

He lit a cigarette and sat on the bed. He had not expected this. He had been prepared to meet the problem when it was presented, but it had come earlier than he had hoped. Tonya knew so much about Nickovitch, a damned lot more than Fletcher. Somehow he had to make sure the past was dead, buried and never resurrected. But the thought of living as a married man also worried him. He was by nature a lone wolf, a man used to his own company and he preferred it that way. He had been trained to be like this, it was the way of life essential to a man in his profession. Having Tonya constantly around him also meant he could never relax, never let his guard down. He was going to be constantly on stage.

He swore, but realised the futility of dwelling on the problem and got up and inspected the adjoining room to occupy his mind. It was the bathroom, equipped with shower, wash basin and toilet. He noticed a shaving kit on a shelf above the wash basin. As he returned to the bedroom Tonya walked in. They stood looking at each other, but there was no display of surprise on Tonya's face.

'Which is yours?' Fletcher asked, looking at the beds.

'It is of no consequence,' she said coolly. She walked over to the dressing table and sat on a stool, studying her face in the mirror.

'After all these years, it is surprising we should end up so close to each other,' Fletcher remarked. He wanted to draw her and get established on the right footing.

'End up?' Tonya asked puzzled. 'You make it sound final. This is only the beginning.'

Fletcher cursed, he hadn't meant it the way she had taken it, but then she didn't think like him. She was Sklevosky, a Russian.

'It isn't really surprising,' she continued in her cryptic flat tones, 'after all, we are supposed to know each other very well.'

Supposed — what did she mean? Did she already suspect him?

'I think we had better understand each other,' Fletcher said firmly. 'The past must be forgotten, it is too dangerous and we cannot afford to make any slips. We must not only play our part, but we must think it also. I shall make certain I act my part without fault. I shall be a reasonably attentive husband to you during the day and evenings.'

She turned to face him.

'So long as you don't expect the same attention in return during the nights,' she said icily.

'Don't worry,' Fletcher said evenly, 'I won't bother you.' He crossed over to the bathroom. At the door he hesitated, 'I am going to have a shower,' he said.

He stripped off and got under the shower. He had got the message across — the past was to be forgotten. But what did she mean, 'we are supposed to know each other very well'? Was it just sarcasm, or did she already have doubts?

He had finished his shower and was drying himself when the bathroom door opened and Tonya entered. He looked up at her, annoyed at the intrusion, but he soon forgot his annoyance when he saw her standing there — she was completely naked. He stared at her more in surprise than curiosity. Her figure was evenly proportioned without any surplus fat and her breasts stood out large and firm. She had broad child-bearing hips, but this did not detract from her physical beauty and her cream coloured skin was flawless.

She looked at him defiantly and he could feel her dark eyes appraising his body.

'So long as we are to live together, we don't want any modesty,' she said mockingly. 'That could also prove dangerous.'

Her tone and warning killed any sexual desires which may have entered his head and as she took her place in the shower he collected his clothes and moved into the bedroom.

Chapter Seven

The evening's television viewing was followed by a period of discussion and it was well into the night when they all retired. The following morning, the class assembled for breakfast with the Smiths and the pattern of instruction previously laid down was strictly adhered to.

The days that followed were long and full. Fortunately, it soon became apparent to Fletcher that neither the Smiths, or any of the agents, had any interest in Dimitri Nickovitch, or anything which had preceded their arrival at the camp. All they were concerned with was familiarising themselves with their new roles and if they criticised him it was for his failure to act in accordance with Paul Adams and not Dimitri Nickovitch. Occasionally they did have political discussions, but as these became a constant reiteration of the communist line Fletcher had little difficulty in appearing as dedicated to their cause as did the other three agents.

Sharing a chalet with Tonya did not prove as menacing as he had anticipated. After the long periods of instruction it purely became a matter of sharing a bedroom. It was a paper marriage without any frills and conversation became reduced to essentials.

There was no modesty or embarrassment, Tonya had seen to that on their first evening together. She had no irritating habits which could offend him, everything she did was neat and efficient and Fletcher made sure he followed a similar code. Even her dislike for him she kept hidden. She had been well trained and moulded in the Soviet pattern — a system which produced hard, ruthless agents, but women of questionable feminine charm.

There were never any periods of relaxation, the Smiths kept them hard at it and the only opportunity Fletcher got to form any opinions of the other agents was by the way they reacted to Smith's instruction.

Timovitch was slow, methodical and cautious. Mikolyn, however, had a more agile brain and was quick to grasp whatever Smith was trying to get over to him. Tonya was shrewd and intelligent and to Fletcher the most dangerous. If anyone was to suspect him it would be her. Not because of her previous knowledge of Nickovitch, but because she appeared more detached and sure of herself than the other two. There were frequent occasions when he caught her studying him closely and it would give him a feeling of disquiet.

All of them, however, were extremely knowledgeable about the west and all that was required from the Smiths was the final setting of their personality and mannerisms to suit their assumed roles. But Smith was a perfectionist and would spend hours going over a simple action or function until he was satisfied it was correct.

Gradually their training began to produce results. Fletcher could see it in the others and knew it was happening to himself. Timovitch became the cheery Cockney chauffeur, Mikolyn the cynical, brash Australian engineer and Tonya the rather haughty wife of a wealthy businessman with a taste for expensive clothes and a confident, superior manner.

Periodically throughout their training Smith fed them further information on the arrangements made to receive them in London, but he only gave the information to the person concerned. This meant that Fletcher learned nothing further about Timovitch or Mikolyn's movements. Nor could he get anything out of Smith about their organisation in London, other than it existed and was preparing the way for them. But their arrangements were a further typical example of the thoroughness of the Soviet Spy System.

A house had been rented on a nine months lease for Fletcher and Tonya in a select area of Redhill in Surrey. It was of medium size and detached — the typical home of a successful commuting businessman. They were shown films of the house and of their office in the city, a drab insignificant-looking building adjoining an empty warehouse in the deserted area near the Royal Victoria Docks. An area where a change of managership would not be noticed.

Their business was not a fabrication, but a legitimate export and import agency founded in 1898. It was a business where personal contact with the clients was not essential and had obviously been used by other agents. Its existence was of immense value in completing the image of authenticity which they were carefully aiming to project.

The K.G.B. didn't produce commando type agents, they produced spies — men and women who had to become an integral part of western society and feed back information. But if the cloak and dagger veil normally attributed to such work was absent, the simplicity and plausibility of the arrangements left a more deadly and sinister impression.

Despite the almost fanatical immersion of the other agents and the Smiths into their work, Fletcher was still given cause to ponder on the uncertainty and danger of his position. The Smiths had occasional visitors to their establishment — visitors who came and went during the hours of darkness. Who they were, or what was the purpose of their clandestine type visits, Fletcher never found out, but each time he heard them arrive it gave him a feeling of trepidation. They had a vast army of spies, police and informers and he knew only too well that if they got wind of even the slightest suspicion they would not hesitate to take him back to the sadistic Colonel Reitzler for further questioning.

Fortunately, graduation day came sooner than he had expected.

One day, towards the end of their fourth week, Smith told them all at breakfast that there was to be no television viewing that evening and that they were to remain in their chalets. No reason was given, but when they returned from their afternoon session in the hangar a large black saloon car stood on the driveway outside the bungalow. The Smiths were entertaining a visitor earlier than usual.

The following morning, when the car was still standing on the driveway, Fletcher realised there was something afoot.

Breakfast was served in their rooms, but soon afterwards Smith appeared and told them to accompany him to the bungalow. He looked subdued and serious and Fletcher was immediately on his guard. When Smith told them why they were going to the bungalow, Fletcher's suspicions were confirmed. They were to meet an emissary from Moscow.

In the bungalow they were directed into the dining room, where sitting waiting for them was Mrs Smith and a man with a lean tanned face and deep-set, powerful brown eyes. They were seated side by side at the far end of the long table, on which lay a number of folders. Fletcher and Tonya were told to sit on two vacant chairs facing Mrs Smith and the stranger, whilst her husband took a side seat.

No introductions were made or any gestures of welcome given and for several minutes there was an uncanny silence in the room as the stranger stared intently at first Fletcher and then Tonya. He was a man in his late fifties with dark brown hair, greying at the edges. He was dressed in an eastern cut suit, but of better quality than the rough material Fletcher had worn. His hands rested on the table and Fletcher noticed his well-manicured nails. He was one of the communist hierarchy. One of the spy masters from the Kremlin.

Fletcher waited apprehensively. Was he supposed to know the man? Had Nickovitch met him before? His description didn't fit any of those given to Fletcher, but then they didn't know all of Nickovitch's contacts. It was a tense moment.

The stranger opened one of his folders and sat silently staring at it, as if comparing what he had seen with the details in his file.

Fletcher glanced at Mrs Smith. Not only was he surprised to see her sitting in an apparent position of authority, but also the change in her appearance. She had no make-up on her face and wore a plain dark grey dress which made her look a lot older and much less attractive, than before.

Finally the stranger spoke.

'You have made excellent progress,' he said in Russian. 'Excellent.'

He was looking directly at Fletcher as he spoke, his eyes searching Fletcher's face as if looking for some sign of reaction. Fletcher didn't flinch a muscle, but he mentally prayed that his progress had not been so outstanding as to warrant suspicion. He was relieved when the stranger turned to Tonya and added: 'Both of you.'

'Thank you, Comrade,' Tonya said.

'It is well because the time has come to put your training to the service of our country.'

Fletcher's pulse quickened. This was what he had hoped for.

'I have your orders from Moscow,' the stranger added.

Tonya gave a stifled gasp and the stranger quickly looked at her. 'Is anything wrong, Comrade?' he asked sharply.

Fletcher held his breath. If she had any doubts about him this was the time for her to voice them.

'No, Comrade,' she replied hastily, 'I had not expected our orders so soon.'

Fletcher relaxed again. She had voiced what he had been thinking.

'There are other circumstances which dictate the time,' the stranger said harshly, 'and I am assured that you are well prepared.' He turned to Mrs Smith. 'That is so?'

'Yes, Comrade,' Mrs Smith replied. 'They have learned quickly. A little more time would be welcomed, but it is not essential.'

She had replied in Russian without any trace of accent and her crisp business-like tones settled any lingering doubts Fletcher still had as to the relative position of Mrs Smith and her husband. Undoubtedly Mrs Smith was in charge and her husband the front man. Again they had not run true to form, again he had underestimated them.

The stranger looked at Fletcher.

'Are you ready, Comrade?'

Fletcher replied firmly, 'Yes, Comrade.'

'Are you sure there is nothing else?' the stranger asked Tonya.

This time she answered with equal firmness.

'No, Comrade. I welcome the opportunity to serve our cause.'

'Good.'

The spy master glanced down at the open folder and then looked at them both again.

'Who is Sir Joseph Manning?' he said.

Fletcher hesitated. He knew the name, but he had to be certain he had learned it from the Smiths and not from previous knowledge. Tonya solved the problem.

'A member of the British Government,' she said.

'Anything else?'

'Connected with defence,' Fletcher added.

'Correct — he is in fact Parliamentary Secretary to the Minister of Defence.'

Having made his statement the stranger paused, but as neither Fletcher or Tonya volunteered any further information he continued: 'Sir Joseph Manning is a Socialist Member of Parliament. He became an M.P. about six years ago. Last year he was appointed Parliamentary Secretary to the Minister of Defence because of his industrial background.'

From a bulky briefcase he produced a thick folder which he placed on the table.

'This is a dossier on Sir Joseph. Every detail about him is in here. For the rest of the day you will study the facts so that you will know Sir Joseph better than he knows himself. We intend to make use of him … soon.'

Fletcher hung on every word. Their gamble was beginning to pay off.

'Your orders are to make the acquaintance of Sir Joseph and his family and cultivate their friendship. When we consider the time is ripe you will get further instructions. You have six months in which to do it, but you must be on friendly terms by the end of next month.' The stranger raised his eyebrows as if inviting comment.

'That does not give us much time,' Fletcher said.

The spy master gave a wry smile.

'I appreciate your concern,' he said evenly, 'but fortunately Sir Joseph is making it a little easier for us. However, I repeat

— you must be on intimate terms with Sir Joseph and his family within six months, even if it means overplaying your hand. If necessary we can always bring you back.' He made a gesture with his hands. 'That is no problem.'

Fletcher was deeply curious. Why Sir Joseph Manning? Why the time limit? Why the lack of concern? This was not usual. Spying was a slow cautious game. This development surprised him.

'You say Sir Joseph is playing into our hands?' Tonya asked calmly.

'Yes. Two weeks ago Sir Joseph had an operation from which he is now recovering. In two days' time he and his family are flying to Spain for a holiday. The British are a peculiar race. Once they get abroad they tend to drop their reserve. In fact, they become quite friendly. The resort where Sir Joseph is staying is also popular with the Germans and as Sir Joseph is not well disposed towards them, he will naturally be more prone to become friendly with one of his own countrymen.'

The rest was left unsaid, but Fletcher understood what was planned. He and Tonya were to join Sir Joseph and his family at their hotel in Spain. What the spy master had said about the British was true enough. It was an ideal opportunity to make their acquaintance.

'Where is the hotel?' he asked.

'S'Agaro. It is a very luxurious hotel. Sir Joseph is a creature of habit; he has been staying at the same hotel for several years now, long before the area became popular. Fortunately for him the price has kept it select.'

He clasped his hands and leaned on the table.

'You leave tonight. You will be smuggled into Barcelona. Two of our agents are returning via that route. When they arrive at Barcelona Airport you will take their place and join a small group of tourists travelling to various resorts along the coast. The travel courier who will be accompanying the party is also one of our agents. Sir Joseph will have already arrived. You will stay at the hotel for two weeks. During that time you must make contact. At the end of two weeks you will fly to London where you will continue to cultivate Sir Joseph and his family. All the necessary arrangements are being made.' He paused. 'You see why it is essential to cut short your training?'

'Yes, Comrade,' Tonya replied dutifully.

'Who is our contact in London?' Fletcher asked.

'By the time you have arrived in London, Comrade Timovitch will also be there — Timovitch will contact you and pass on all orders.'

'What if there should be any mishap with Comrade Timovitch?' Fletcher persisted.

Mrs Smith answered his question.

'There won't be,' she said confidently, 'but if there is you will be contacted.' Her reply gave Fletcher the impression that she was well acquainted with the organisation in London.

'Now for the details,' the stranger said. 'Comrade Smith,' he indicated Mr Smith, 'will prepare your wardrobe and luggage. You will leave tonight after your evening meal. A car will take you to Constanta where you will join a ship sailing for Barcelona. On board the ship you will remain in your cabin at all times.' He smiled. 'We don't want you to get a suntan just yet. At Barcelona our agent will look after you and get you to the airport. When you arrive at London you will collect the keys of your house and office from an Estate Agent in Redhill. You have been briefed on these matters?'

'Yes, Comrade,' Tonya replied.

'You will be given sufficient money at Barcelona and a number of travellers cheques. Also your passports.'

'What about money when we arrive in London?' Fletcher asked.

'A joint account has been opened for you in Barclays Bank in Redhill and a sum of three thousand pounds is being deposited in your favour. If you should require any further amounts you can arrange this with Comrade Timovitch.'

As the spy master reeled out his instructions in his quiet and efficient manner it became clear that this was no last minute decision. The elaborate precautions they had taken to set them up in London seemed to indicate that it was all part of a carefully designed plan of campaign which was aimed at something bigger than the normal run of the mill spy work.

Finally the spy master stood up.

'I will be here until midday,' he said, 'should you want to ask any further questions. Otherwise Comrade Smith will look after you.' He turned to Mrs Smith who had also stood up. 'Will the others be at work?' he asked.

'Yes.'

'Good. I want to visit your village again. We will see them there.'

He left the room with Mrs Smith following close behind. Just as there had been no word of welcome when Fletcher and Tonya had entered the room, similarly there was no word of encouragement when the stranger left. The K.G.B. functioned like a machine and machines had no feelings.

Smith stood up and told them he would go and attend to their luggage and wardrobe. He seemed eager to get out of their company.

Fletcher collected the dossier on Sir Joseph. He was very curious to find out what kind of man he was. When he turned to Tonya, however, he was both surprised and alarmed to see her openly staring at him. Her face was expressionless, but her eyes looked intense. It was as if she was making a last minute appreciation of him.

Their eyes met and Fletcher returned her gaze defiantly. He was so close to getting out of their tight grip. So close! This was the final hurdle.

'Is something troubling you, Comrade?' he asked sarcastically, hoping to draw her.

But she didn't accept the bait and continued to stare at him. Finally she turned her eyes away from him. 'Let us make a start,' she said in an icy tone which gave little hope for a friendly partnership. But she had made her decision and Fletcher knew he would have no further trouble from her. He turned his attention to Sir Joseph Manning.

The dossier on Sir Joseph was a complete factual report on the man's life, both private and political. It even presumed to predict his future. Much of the information was obviously so private as to have only been written by someone very close to the man. A fact which Fletcher mentally stored away and made him wonder if the Communists did not already have an agent close to the man.

Sir Joseph was sixty five years of age and for the past six years had been a Socialist Member of Parliament for a constituency in the Birmingham area. He had been born of humble parents and his life history read like a do it yourself success story. From factory floor to management and from management to his own business, a business which had mushroomed in the late thirties and during the war had become an integral part of a munition supply group.

His transition into politics started during the war when he had been co-opted onto a number of local committees where he had excelled himself in the field of man management. The reward for his war work had been his knighthood. After the war he became a Socialist Councillor and finally in the 1960 general election had won a marginal seat for the Socialist Party and entered Parliament.

As a Socialist he was generally in the centre, but on certain issues he displayed a strong left-wing tendency. He was well known for his support of peaceful co-existence and had strongly opposed the United States policies on a number of occasions.

In the Socialist Party he was respected, but treated with caution. For a Socialist a title and a business interest were not the ideal assets to have. With the opposition he was liked, but his rather naïve faith in peaceful co-existence made them suspicious. In all he trod a rather lonely political path.

His private life had suffered a number of setbacks. His wife had died suddenly in the year preceding the war and during the latter days of the war his son had been killed on a flying mission over Germany. Both deaths had affected him considerably.

In 1950 Sir Joseph had remarried and was now living in Guildford in Surrey. He had a son, Peter aged twelve years and a daughter, Susan, by his first wife, who acted as his secretary.

Fletcher gave a smile as he read the report. They were practically going to be neighbours. A fact which, no doubt, the Soviets had carefully planned.

Sir Joseph had few hobbies. He read, played an occasional round of golf, enjoyed a game of bridge and took a typical family man's interest in photography. His work kept him too busy for other pursuits.

The historical facts about Sir Joseph stopped short at his entry into hospital for what was referred to as an abdominal operation. There was no mention anywhere of his convalescing holiday in Spain. The sudden decision of Moscow to cut short their training suggested that it had been a last minute move on Sir Joseph's part and again Fletcher had cause to consider how well informed Moscow was being kept of his movements.

Fletcher stopped reading the report to study a recent family photograph of the Mannings.

Sir Joseph was a tall, well-made man with a bluff, friendly face and a boxer's nose. His wife looked a number of years younger than her husband and had a pleasant round face which gave the impression of a friendly and capable woman. His daughter, Susan, had the attractive and classical features of a model. She was tall, like her father, but slim. She didn't bear any resemblance to her father and had rather striking features with high cheekbones and long fair hair. Her half-brother, Peter, however, did take after his father and looked a normal healthy child.

Fletcher looked at the fat dossier. Every facet of Sir Joseph's life would be there. A clinical report on his work, his speeches and his family. Why? What had aroused the Soviets' interest in the man? Was he a Communist sympathiser? Was he a man who could be won over to their cause? Or was he an innocent about to be dragged into the net of Communist intrigue?

He glanced at Tonya who was methodically storing away the facts in her orderly mind. She also puzzled him. Was she so hard and unyielding as she appeared? What was she thinking and feeling? Was she apprehensive? Anxious? Or had she been so well indoctrinated by the Communists to make her immune to such normal feelings?

He sighed. In a few months he would know all the answers — if he didn't make any mistakes.

Chapter Eight

They left the Smiths during the evening and drove nonstop across the heart of Romania to the port of Constanta on the Black Sea, where they boarded a small coaster which was preparing to leave on the morning tide.

For two days and two nights they remained in their cabin — a noisy, artificially lit sweat box. The rigour of the journey tried both their patience. The confined space made exercise impossible and the constant throb of the engines killed any thought of normal conversation. The smell and the heat combined to make it a living hell.

For Fletcher, however, the fact that he was on the boat at all more than compensated for the discomfort of his quarters. It could easily have been so different. That Tonya had not questioned his identity, he credited to Nickovitch's eight years of separation and her blind faith in her superiors in Moscow. Eight years was a long time and a person could change considerably during those years, both physically and mentally. It could well account for any differences she might notice between the Nickovitch of her youth and Fletcher's impersonation. But he would still have to take care.

Fletcher made no plans and had none prepared. Nor had he any contacts in Spain or in England. His own web of agents and informers was spread over the Balkans and his own link with the British Government was through the military attachés of the various embassies. No arrangements had been made for contacting British Security either for fear the Communists had broken him under interrogation and it had been agreed that there would be no interference with his work until he could be of no further service.

Fletcher couldn't serve two masters at once and the extent of his success depended on how well he pleased his Soviet masters. He was now one of them. However, British Intelligence had engineered the whole scheme and they would be on the look-out for him. As soon as he exposed himself, London would get to know.

The journey did provide an opportunity for them to get used to each other's company, but their relationship remained unchanged. They were two Soviet agents who had to work together and it was kept at that level.

At Barcelona they were smuggled ashore during the night and taken to a photographic shop at the end of a tree-lined boulevard. In the small room at the rear of the shop a local agent was waiting for them and gave them their final instructions.

The following morning the exchange with the two returning agents was carried out with almost military precision. Fletcher and Tonya were driven to the airport in a taxi and their arrival timed to coincide with arrival of the plane from London. They were dressed in similar clothes as their exchange would be wearing and alongside them were their expensive-looking cases adorned with labels of the Continental Travel Agency.

At the airport they left their cases in the taxi and slipped into the terminal building by a side door which backed on to the rear stalls of a tourist shop. No sooner had they taken their place when another couple appeared around the end of the stall. It was their exchange. They were discussing the various articles for sale in a rather loud voice. Fletcher and Tonya took over their discussion and strolled casually into the hallway.

In the middle of the foyer was a small group of tourists and the courier who was with them called Fletcher and Tonya over to join them. She was a slim, plain looking girl in her early twenties. On her jacket was a badge of the Continental Travel Agency with her name, 'Miss Webster', printed across the centre. She scolded them politely for having left the party and handed Fletcher a folder containing his return flight tickets and travellers cheques. Fletcher put them in his pocket and he and Tonya melted into the small tourist group waiting to be taken to their resort.

The S'Agaro Hotel was a luxury hotel with its own swimming pool and every creature comfort. It was set back from the beach and surrounded by watered lawns and palm trees.

But the splendour of their accommodation was wasted on Fletcher and Tonya. From the moment they had accomplished their exchange at the airport they set about their mission with a singularity of purpose. No matter what Tonya's true feelings may have been towards Fletcher, she nevertheless accepted him instantly as a business partner and became the sophisticated Mrs Paul Adams to such an extent that if the consummation of their marriage had been a public event she would have performed the act without hesitation. The only time she dropped her pose was when they discussed their work, when once again she would become the cold, calculating communist agent.

The hotel was busy, but not crowded. There were only a handful of British guests, the remainder being Continentals, of whom the majority were Germans.

Gradually the British guests began to acknowledge each other's presence. At first it was a formal good morning and good evening, but slowly they became more adventuresome.

Only the Mannings remained aloof. They kept entirely to themselves and didn't even respect the normal courtesies. It was soon apparent that making their acquaintance was not going to be so simple as originally anticipated.

Sir Joseph looked much older than his photographs and more distinguished, with steel blue eyes and grey hair. His wife, in contrast, looked quite young. She was an attractive woman, full of sparkle, who organised her family with enthusiasm and kept an ever watchful eye on them. Susan Manning was as striking as her photographs had indicated and had the same steel blue eyes as her father. Her half-brother was a pleasant youth, full of energy, but well behaved.

With the Mannings, however, was a tall gangling man in his early thirties. His presence puzzled Fletcher and his over pompous manner and exaggerated accent irritated him. He had not been expected and his presence could prove a drawback. He added that extra bit of company to the Mannings which could stop them looking for it elsewhere.

Fletcher and Tonya bided their time like two hawks watching their prey.

During this waiting period they followed the normal pursuits of two holidaymakers. They visited the local shops, drank in the small bars, sunbathed on the beach and swam in the sea. They even became friendly with a Scots couple, Ian and Mary Grey. This was not by accident, but by design. When they started their operations in London they would need to cultivate a wide diversity of friendships and acquaintances as an innocent screen for their work and when they learned that the Greys had only recently left Scotland to live in North London they were considered ideal candidates.

But the tentacles of the Kremlin still managed to reach its way into this rather sleepy Spanish resort in the form of Miss

Webster. Her daily visits to the hotel had a more sinister purpose than the innocent duties she performed. Despite her lack of years and youthful appearance, she was nevertheless the eyes and ears of the party. Through her Moscow was being kept informed of their progress. On the fourth day of their stay she even brought the impatience of the Kremlin out into the open.

She joined them on the beach and after exchanging a few brief pleasantries brought the conversation around to the real purpose of her visit.

'Have you made many friends?' she asked.

'Yes,' Tonya replied. 'Most of the British that are staying here are quite friendly. The Scots couple join us frequently.'

But Miss Webster was not interested in the Scots couple, or the guests generally.

'Isn't that Sir Joseph Manning and his family over there?' she asked.

'Yes,' Tonya again replied. 'They spend most of their time on the beach.'

'Have you been introduced to them yet?'

Fletcher spoke for the first time.

'No,' he said. 'They keep themselves very much to themselves.'

'The British can be like that,' she said with a bland smile, 'but often they welcome other people making the first move.'

Fletcher felt himself becoming annoyed. She was only a slip of a girl, but she was telling him how to do his job. To force their attentions on the Mannings would be fatal. It was a game of patience. Tonya also appeared to resent her remarks.

'We are well aware of that,' Tonya snapped. 'When the right opportunity presents itself we will make a move.'

Miss Webster was not abashed.

'I'm so pleased,' she said. 'I do want you to enjoy yourselves and make friends.' She stood up. 'Oh, by the way, I was told to warn you that the opposition have their representative at the hotel.'

Fletcher looked up, surprised. He had not expected this.

'Who?' he asked.

'I'm afraid we don't know. However, you have nothing to fear. Your stories are watertight.' She looked again at the Manning's party. 'Who is that man with Sir Joseph?' she asked.

'Buckley,' Fletcher said. He had found that out from a casual glance at the head waiter's list. 'But who he is, or what he does, we have yet to find out.'

'Buckley,' she repeated the name. It would appear in her next report.

She left soon afterwards, but promised to return.

Fletcher forestalled any discussion with Tonya by going for a swim. He wanted time to think. He swam out to the hotel raft and climbed aboard. Why had the British sent one of their agents to the hotel? he wondered. Sir Joseph wasn't so important as to warrant protection. Had they anticipated that the Communists would try to contact him? or were they, in fact, suspicious of Sir Joseph? Had his holiday been a sudden impulse after all? Or a cleverly designed scheme to provide Fletcher and Tonya an opportunity of becoming friendly? And why were the Soviets so interested in Sir Joseph? What was there about the man that should suddenly attract the attention of both Intelligence Services?

He gazed across at the beach where the majority of the hotel guests were arrayed. Who was this British agent? he wondered. He noticed Tonya had been joined by the Greys. Was Ian Grey all that he purported to be? Was he the rising insurance executive that he claimed? But he was too knowledgeable on insurance matters and had given too many particulars about himself which could be verified and checked. He discounted him.

He turned his attention to Buckley, but soon discounted him also. He was a little too obvious and he had too high a regard for British Intelligence to accept the obvious.

Mentally he went through the guests, but soon came to the conclusion that the answer could not be found by deduction. It could be anyone, even one of the Continentals. The British Government had a lot on their payroll.

He decided to forget about it. He didn't wish to make contact with British Intelligence and it was unlikely they would interfere with him. In fact, it was all for the good. His progress would now be reported back to London as well as Moscow.

He swam back to the beach and rejoined Tonya. She was alone.

'Mrs Grey suggested a game of bridge this evening,' Tonya said.

Fletcher rubbed himself with a towel. Sir Joseph was a keen bridge player. It could be a good move.

'You agreed?' he asked.

'Yes. The Mannings also play bridge.'

'Make sure we play in the lounge, close to the bar, so they will see us.'

'Have you any idea who their agent could be?'

'None at all,' he replied honestly. 'I don't think it matters, if we play our hands right.' He put on his shirt. 'We'll give it one more day. If nothing breaks then we will make a move.'

The evening's bridge helped them to practice what the Smiths had taught them and proved successful on that account, but as for flaunting their interest in the game in front of Sir Joseph it was a failure. At dinner the Mannings were joined by two Spanish guests and were not seen afterwards in either the bar or the lounge.

Consequently, the following day they settled themselves on the beach in their customary place ready to make plans.

'We will start by going through their daily routine,' Fletcher said. 'They haven't varied it very much. They have breakfast round about nine o'clock…'

'Sir Joseph goes for a walk before that,' Tonya interrupted.

Fletcher looked at her.

'Sir Joseph rises early each morning. About seven-thirty. He walks the full length of the bay and then rejoins the family in their rooms.'

Tonya had not been wasting her time. She was also an early riser. Now Fletcher knew why.

'Carry on,' he said.

She gave him the facts as if she was reading from a book, she had missed nothing. The Mannings had kept to a regular pattern of movement centred around the hotel, the beach, the swimming pool and the cocktail bar, with an occasional visit to the village shops. Tonya knew all their timings and also their drinking habits. So did Fletcher, but he still admired her thoroughness.

'Lady Manning has made an appointment at the hairdressers; for this evening at seven,' Tonya added. 'Also for next Wednesday at the same time. I also have a hair appointment for this evening at seven.'

'Is that wise?' Fletcher asked.

'We must make a move.'

It sounded like an order. He looked at her face and knew it was.

He turned his attention to the Mannings. There must be some way they could establish themselves with them without making it obvious. He watched the boy go into the sea and swim to the raft. He was a fine little swimmer.

Thoughtfully, he lit a cigarette. With the stranger in their company it was more difficult than ever to start up a casual conversation with them in the bar or lounge, but Tonya's suggestion didn't appeal to him. It was too direct. He saw Sir Joseph go to the water's edge and call out to his son.

He is very fond of the boy, he thought … very fond.

An idea began to take shape.

'Have you noticed how keen the boy is on swimming?' he asked.

'Yes, so is the daughter.'

'What does the boy do when they return to the hotel after tea?'

'Goes to the swimming pool.'

'By himself?'

'Yes. Sir Joseph reads in the lounge.'

'So he is in the pool by himself,' he said thoughtfully, 'and the pool is not used by many others at that time?'

'No. He has it to himself.'

'That is it, then,' Fletcher said eagerly. 'I will start having a swim in the pool round about the same time. We will get to Sir Joseph through the boy.'

Tonya was not so enthusiastic.

'It will take time,' she said.

Fletcher didn't agree. He was already one jump ahead.

'The hotel hires out aqualung equipment,' he explained, 'and unless I am mistaken that boy will be very keen to have a go.'

He waited for her reaction. There was just a possibility that skin diving had not been part of their training.

But Tonya was not suspicious.

'What about my hair appointment?' she asked.

'Leave it,' Fletcher said, 'but don't attempt to establish contact. We will try my way first.'

That afternoon Fletcher hired the aqualung equipment from the hotel and went swimming in the coves at the end of the bay. On his return he made sure he passed close to where the Mannings were sitting so that the boy could see the equipment. Later he went to the swimming pool, but as several other guests were there, as well as the boy, he made no move.

The following day he again hired the equipment and on his return he noticed the boy looking at him with interest.

The fish was beginning to nibble at the bait.

That evening when Fletcher went to the pool only the boy was using it. In next to no time he had made friends with him and together they swam and played around in the water.

At a suitable moment Fletcher made his offer to take him skin diving. An invitation which the boy accepted with enthusiasm. When Fletcher left the pool to dry himself he was well satisfied with his evening's work. As he collected his towel he noticed Sir Joseph had appeared. He was standing at the end of the pool still wearing his glasses and carrying a bundle of newspapers under his arm. If he noticed Fletcher's presence he made no sign to acknowledge the fact.

Fletcher watched the boy come out of the water and dash over to his father. He could hear him telling his father about his offer to take him skin diving. He saw Sir Joseph wrap a towel around his son and say something. What he said Fletcher had no idea, but the look that came over the boy's face made him assume Sir Joseph was not being co-operative. He decided to act. There was no one around. They were not being observed. He could afford to take a risk.

He walked over to them.

'I don't think we have met,' he said, extending his hand. 'My name is Paul Adams.'

Sir Joseph had no alternative but to accept the handshake and introduce himself.

'Manning,' he said gruffly and added almost apologetically, 'Sir Joseph Manning.'

'How do you do?' Fletcher said.

'Please, Daddy, may I go with Mr Adams?' the boy pleaded.

'I am sure you will only be holding Mr Adams back,' his father muttered.

'On the contrary,' Fletcher said, 'I will be only too pleased to teach your son how to use the aqualung equipment. He is a fine swimmer and will enjoy it and you need not be concerned. I have had a lot of experience with the equipment.'

Again the boy pleaded with his father and in the face of such opposition it would have taken a very stern parent to refuse. Sir Joseph relented and rather begrudgingly gave his consent. The boy beamed at Fletcher.

'I will see you at ten o'clock in the morning,' Fletcher said. 'In the lounge.'

He collected his bathrobe and left them by the pool. Sir Joseph was going to be a hard nut to crack, but crack him he would and the boy was going to be his instrument. He didn't intend to let the fish get off the hook.

As events turned out the following day proved more successful than either Fletcher or Tonya had expected.

When Fletcher went to collect the equipment from the hotel porter, he found not only Peter Manning waiting for him, but also his sister, Susan. She was wearing a pale blue two piece swimsuit which was designed to show off her tanned body to its best advantage.

'This is my sister, Susan,' Peter Manning said eagerly.

She held out her hand and flashed a smile.

'How do you do, Mr Adams. I hope you don't mind if I tag along, but I would also like to do some skin diving.'

Fletcher looked at her blonde, tanned features and slim, supple body. If she wanted to play watch dog to her brother it was all right by him — more than all right.

'Delighted,' he said.

They collected their cylinders and masks and went to the far end of the bay where they could practice in privacy. Susan Manning, like her brother, was a good swimmer and it was not long before they became accustomed to the equipment. By the end of the morning they were becoming sufficiently expert and enthusiastic to want to venture further afield and arrangements were made to meet the following morning. Fletcher also made sure that by the end of the lesson he and Susan Manning were on less formal terms than they had been at the beginning.

But the surprise of the day came with Tonya. She had gone to the beach prepared to spend the morning reading, but Lady Manning, seeing that Tonya was by herself and no doubt feeling under an obligation, had invited her to join them. This was an unexpected opportunity. Unwittingly Lady Manning had breached the dam — the flood was to follow.

No matter what other intentions she may have had, Tonya would not have let their acquaintance end there. However, Tonya had been well trained in human psychology and current affairs and Lady Manning soon discovered that she had acquired a very interesting and interested, companion. A companion, strangely enough, whose tastes and interests were very similar to her own.

The following day the same performance was repeated and after dinner that evening they even joined the Mannings in the cocktail bar. By now the Mannings were well and truly in the net.

But Fletcher did not forget the Greys. They were going to need them in London. Also Ian Grey was a good conversationalist, as was his wife. Something Sir Joseph was not. So Fletcher introduced them to the Mannings and encouraged them into their company and in so doing paved the way for further contact in London on two accounts.

The tall thin man was introduced as Phillip Buckley, a family friend, but it soon came to light that he was also a political correspondent for a prominent London newspaper. He was a product of the London School of Economics, but if his political views were similar to Sir Joseph's his affected manner belied the fact. Fortunately, he was only staying a further few days as he had to go to Madrid on an assignment for his paper. During the remainder of his stay at the hotel Fletcher had little contact with the man.

Susan Manning and her brother took up most of Fletcher's time. But Buckley was too valuable a contact to pass over, so Tonya made up for Fletcher's social shortcomings and became quite friendly with him.

When eventually Buckley departed for Madrid the Mannings drew closer to Fletcher and Tonya…

At first, Sir Joseph had little to say in company. He was sociable when the occasion demanded, but reluctant to hold the conversation as well as he could with his knowledge of affairs. He was content to let his wife have the limelight whilst he remained aloof, as if conscious of his political office.

As the days passed, however, Fletcher gradually got to know the man better and found him a very astute, knowledgeable man and a deep thinker.

Miss Webster still made her daily visits to the hotel, but made no further move to engage either Fletcher or Tonya in conversation and Fletcher could only assume that Moscow was satisfied with their progress.

By the end of their holiday all their time was being spent in the company of the Mannings and even when the time came for the Mannings to leave tentative arrangements were made to meet again in London. They had achieved all that Moscow had expected of them.

Fletcher, however, felt disappointed. Sir Joseph had made no move or said anything which would help to explain why the Communists were interested in him, or why British Intelligence were watching him. He was as much in the dark as he had been when they arrived. But was Sir Joseph?

Chapter Nine

The Mannings return to London was swiftly followed by Fletcher and Tonya. The only witness to their flight from Spain was the ever-observing Miss Webster at Barcelona airport.

At London, they passed through the customs apparently unnoticed and without a hitch. They were two everyday tourists returning from a holiday. But when they went to Redhill to collect the keys of their house and to take up residence, they found their contact had been warned of their arrival. The hidden eye of the Soviet spy system had observed their arrival at the airport. Fletcher wondered whether British Security were as equally efficient.

Everything was laid on for them. Their house was furnished like a show piece and in the double garage stood the status symbols of a man of Fletcher's supposed means — two cars, a Daimler and a small Riley.

With typical thoroughness and determination they set about familiarising themselves with their new surroundings. It wasn't easy. The Smiths had shown them how, but it had been in the seclusion of a deserted hangar. In the suburbs of London the pace was much faster and their observers more numerous. They made mistakes. Stupid mistakes which irritated each other because they knew they could prove fatal if they occurred at the wrong moment.

Eventually they ventured to their office in London, at first by train and later by car. Here again they had to adjust themselves to the seething masses of people and constant flow of traffic.

Fortunately their office was in a secluded area in Canning Town. It was only a two-roomed office, but adjoined an empty warehouse which belonged to the firm. But if it was like an oasis in the wilderness to Tonya, it was anything but to Fletcher.

Nickovitch had been trained to work in this office, so had Tonya, but he hadn't. Even though their legitimate business was almost insignificant, it nevertheless existed, and Fletcher quickly realised it could prove fatal. On the pretence of familiarising himself with the numerous files which adorned the walls he let Tonya attend to the outstanding enquiries which had accumulated and closely watched and learned from her.

During this initial period of climatization they didn't lose contact with either the Mannings or the Greys. They couldn't afford to. Shortly after their arrival Susan Manning phoned them and it was an indication of how well they had impressed the Mannings that she made the first move. The reason for her telephone call was obscure, but out of it came an agreement to spend an evening in town with her parents during the following week.

The Greys were given almost as equal priority as the Mannings. They were so far divorced from what was taking place and so ignorant and unsuspecting of any form of intrigue, that their company could be enjoyed in a more relaxed atmosphere. Consequently, Fletcher and Tonya made use of them as target practice. They both entertained the Greys and in turn were entertained by them.

In readiness for when contact was made with Timovitch, they set about preparing a detailed report of their work in Spain. Fletcher concentrated on his discussions with Sir Joseph and Tonya made general observations. Fortunately, Sir Joseph had said nothing which had not already been published in the press, or of which Moscow would not have been already informed.

One of Tonya's observations, however, took him by surprise. She expressed the opinion that Susan Manning was attracted to him. Fletcher questioned her about it, but she was adamant that it existed. She saw it from a detached viewpoint, whereas he was too closely involved. It explained her constant keenness to go swimming when on holiday and her early telephone call as soon as they had arrived in London.

Fletcher accepted her reasoning and hoped she was correct. He was prepared to use any tactics to achieve their object and that included exploiting any feelings Susan Manning might have towards him.

The typed report was photographed and the original destroyed. The camera which Fletcher used was the only piece of sophisticated spy equipment he had been given by the Soviets. It had a special delicate lens and the camera fitted neatly into his silver plated hair brush.

The evening in town with the Mannings did not turn out as originally planned. At the last minute Lady Manning phoned full of apologies that Sir Joseph was unable to join them as he was involved in a late sitting in the House. Rather than let the opportunity pass of putting the Mannings to a social debt, Fletcher insisted that Lady Manning and Susan still joined them.

So the evening out took place. Susan Manning looked radiant and was obviously pleased to be in their company — a fact which Tonya did not fail to later pass comment on. Lady Manning was equally delighted with the evening and if Sir Joseph was not physically with them his presence was still felt. Such phrases as 'Sir Joseph thinks this' or 'Daddy says that' rolled into the conversation with regularity and they learned more about his views and opinions from his family than they would have done from the man himself.

But it was obvious from their discussions that he was going to be a difficult man to cultivate. Sir Joseph was man of prominent position in the city, whereas Fletcher and Tonya, even with their respectable wealthy background, were one of thousands. Sir Joseph was an extremely busy man and in no way could the business of Westminster be linked with the affairs of a small export and import business in Canning Town. Their only common ground with the man was on holiday in Spain and its significance would diminish with the passing of time. Their only hope was to endear themselves to his wife and daughter and keep their friendship alive through them.

Consequently, they made certain that the evening with them in the city was a success. Like everything they did they carefully planned it before it took place. The show and the restaurant were selected to suit the tastes of Lady Manning and her daughter and even the various topics of conversation which were initiated by Fletcher and Tonya were carefully selected beforehand. Unknowingly Lady Manning and her daughter had been 'conned' by two experts.

Despite the unity Fletcher shared with Tonya towards their work, their normal personal relationship was one of contrasts and became a constant source of concern to Fletcher. In company, Tonya appeared completely at ease with him. She talked, laughed and acted her part superbly, but immediately they were by themselves her attitude changed and she became stiff, formal and unapproachable.

There was a veil of uncertainty about their relationship. Fletcher puzzled her, he was aware of this, but without knowing the true personality of Nickovitch he was helpless to know what to do. Occasionally he would find her watching him, or she would give him a sudden look of surprise and he would realise that something he had done or said had aroused her curiosity.

But he felt certain she didn't suspect the truth and so long as they never resurrected the past he felt reasonably safe. Their work was only planned to last six months and each day brought him nearer his goal.

Contact with the rest of the spy ring was made in July. In answer to a phone call the slow Australian drawl that Mikolyn had perfected came over the wire. He introduced himself as the son of a business client who had been given their address by his father in order that he could pass on his father's best wishes. Fletcher responded accordingly and after enquiring after his father's health invited Mikolyn to spend an evening with them. Mikolyn readily accepted and agreed to visit them the following evening.

When Mikolyn arrived Fletcher took an instant dislike to him. During their training with the Smiths there had been little opportunity to get to know the man, but here in London he was cocky, oversure of himself and contemptuous of the British. He derided them for the ease in which he had entered the country and set himself up. Such a thing could never have happened in the Soviet Union.

Fletcher played along with him, but Tonya harshly warned him to be cautious, a remark which Mikolyn strongly resented. His face hardened and a cruel look came into his eyes. She need have no fear on his account, he told her savagely, he would not make any mistakes. In that brief encounter Fletcher realised how ruthless he could be. He was a man not to be taken lightly.

For the rest of his visit they discussed only business. Mikolyn was in contact with Timovitch and would let Fletcher know when and how Timovitch wanted to meet them. In the meantime, any information had to be channelled through Mikolyn, so Fletcher handed over the microfilms of their report on progress so far.

No information was disclosed as to Timovitch's whereabouts or how either of them had entered the country. All they did learn was that Mikolyn had been in the country for about two weeks and had spent the first week touring the countryside taking photographs. He was staying at the Dominion Club, a residential club used mainly by overseas students and was employed by a firm of consulting engineers. A firm which had a number of Government projects on its drawing boards.

Fletcher was puzzled at his open contact with them until he learned that Mikolyn, like themselves, had orders to cultivate the Mannings. Not Sir Joseph or Lady Manning, but their daughter Susan. The web around the Mannings was being woven in many directions, and in a hurry, and Fletcher's orders from Timovitch were to introduce Mikolyn to his prey.

They discussed the task facing them. Susan Manning was young and enjoyed life. She was at the age and of the social position when pleasure seeking was paramount. She was not without friends, both male and female and Mikolyn would have his work cut out. But his great asset was his assumed Australian nationality. It gave him that little bit of difference which could well appeal to Susan Manning. He was also not unattractive to women.

There was one other factor which Tonya did not overlook — Susan Manning's interest in Fletcher. If Tonya was correct then a little encouragement from Fletcher would be helpful. They decided to play on this. Mikolyn was to be introduced as the son of a business client in Australia. A business client who could be very helpful to Fletcher. If Susan Manning was to help him entertain Mikolyn she would be doing him a great service.

The films taken on their holiday in Spain had been developed and offered an ideal excuse for inviting the Mannings to their home — and to launch Mikolyn. The rest would be up to him. To make the gathering appear even more innocent it was decided to also invite the Greys.

Consequently, the following morning Tonya phoned both Lady Manning and Mary Grey. They both professed a desire to see the films and the following Sunday morning was considered an ideal time. In her telephone conversation Tonya let it be known that they were also entertaining a young man from Australia.

It was a warm, sunny morning on the Sunday and Fletcher and Tonya prepared for a party on the lawn to follow the film show. Mikolyn arrived early and helped them prepare the setting.

When the Mannings did arrive Sir Joseph was once again absent. He sent his apologies, but he had certain business matters to attend to. Although his presence was not essential for the purpose of their party, Fletcher was becoming more than concerned. He had made no direct contact with Sir Joseph since his return from Spain. Soon the Parliamentary recess was due and the Mannings had inferred that they would be leaving the city. He had to establish his friendship with Sir Joseph further before then or Moscow would become impatient.

Susan Manning was his only hope. To her he over-exaggerated his regret that her father had been unable to join them. He pretended to have a deep respect and liking for her father and he hoped Sir Joseph would have lunch with him soon. He also let her know how useful the Australian could be to his business interests in Sydney and any help she could give in entertaining him would be appreciated. He put the messages tactfully and delicately and hoped she would react accordingly.

As for Mikolyn, he was both charming and entertaining. He made no effort to hide his interest in Susan Manning and if she resented his constant attentions she didn't show it.

Ian Grey was more reserved than he had been on previous occasions and confessed to a number of business worries. However, all things considered, it was a successful social gathering, but whether Mikolyn could progress further remained to be seen.

Chapter Ten

A cryptic telephone conversation with Mikolyn soon after they had launched him was the start of further activity. A friend wished to discuss some export business and Fletcher's firm had been recommended. As this friend was only available in the evenings it had been suggested that he should visit Fletcher at his office the following evening at seven o'clock. The real meaning was obvious. Timovitch wanted to make personal contact. But the meeting place was unexpected. Although their office was in a quiet location it was nevertheless exposed.

But Fletcher had underestimated Timovitch. At seven the following evening, the peace of their backwater surroundings was gradually disturbed. At first it was an occasional vehicle and then more vehicles. When Fletcher glanced out of their office window and saw numerous small groups of people hurrying along the road, he realised why the meeting had been arranged in their office. It was close to the West Ham Greyhound Stadium where track meetings were held two nights a week. Timovitch would not be noticed in the crowd which hurried to and from the meeting.

Timovitch entered their office from the adjoining warehouse, a building which had a small entrance door in a narrow side lane. He looked fit and greeted them warmly, shaking their hands. It was the first sign of any display of feelings by the Soviets since Fletcher had joined them.

He was wearing a drab looking, striped brown suit and cloth cap which all helped to build up the image of the ordinary working-class man, as did his cockney accent, but immediately he entered the room he was a changed man. After he had greeted them his eyes surveyed the room critically.

'Safe?' he asked.

'Yes,' Tonya replied confidently.

Timovitch sat down.

'Moscow is pleased with your progress in Spain,' he said.

'Good,' Tonya replied.

'But you have had no further contact with Sir Joseph since you arrived in London.'

Timovitch's statement dispelled any hopes that it was going to be a friendly get together. It was like a douche of cold water. His tone, despite his accent, had been sharp and critical.

'We have tried,' Fletcher said.

'You have not tried hard enough,' Timovitch snapped.

'We arranged an evening in town and Sir Joseph had to cancel at the last moment,' Tonya explained. 'We also invited him to our home when we introduced Vincent, but again he had to decline because of business.'

'I do not want excuses,' Timovitch said icily, 'only results.'

Moscow was becoming a hard task master, Fletcher thought. The stakes must be high. He had expected some such reaction, but still felt annoyed. Their progress so far exceeded his earlier expectations. But he knew it would be in vain to argue with Timovitch. He was only passing on orders.

'I have suggested having lunch with Sir Joseph, to his daughter,' Fletcher explained.

Timovitch seized on it.

'Follow it up,' he ordered, 'and it must be soon. This coming Sunday the Mannings are giving a cocktail party for some of Sir Joseph's political friends. I want you to be present.'

'It will be difficult,' Fletcher said thoughtfully, 'we can't go uninvited.'

'In that case make certain you are invited.'

'How?'

'Susan Manning.'

It was Tonya who had mentioned her name.

Timovitch looked at her.

'She has been the most co-operative,' she explained.

Timovitch shrugged. He was not interested in tactics, only results. He turned to Fletcher.

'Hugh Davies will be at the cocktail party. I want you to meet him. He is a veteran M.P. and a useful man to know.'

'Anything else?' Fletcher asked.

Timovitch hesitated.

'Yes,' he said briefly. 'Panama.'

Fletcher looked up sharply. So did Tonya. Panama had suddenly become the focus of world attention because of a revolutionary movement which had seized part of the country. But there had been no indication that the movement was communist-inspired and Britain certainly wasn't involved. Why were the Soviets suddenly beginning to show interest? he wondered.

'Within the next twenty four hours the Americans are expected to move out of the Canal Zone and occupy the country,' Timovitch explained. 'If they do I want to know what the official attitude of the British Government is to their move. Also the views of Sir Joseph and any other political figures.'

So another name was about to be added to the growing list of international crisis areas, Fletcher thought. Another flare up, another period of tension. So much for peaceful co-existence and co-operation. Timovitch's pre-knowledge of the Americans' intention was sufficient evidence for Fletcher to make him realise that the Communists were behind the whole business.

'You are well informed,' he said.

Timovitch looked at him long and hard.

'Let us say Moscow is well informed,' he said.

Fletcher let the matter drop. It wasn't healthy to show an inquisitive mind. All he was expected to do was to obey orders. But he had even more cause to wonder on how well informed they were when Timovitch started to brief them on Sir Joseph's movements during the Parliamentary recess, which was due to commence the following week.

'On the third of next month,' he explained, 'Sir Joseph and his family are leaving London and spending two weeks in his constituency in Birmingham. After that they are off to Scotland to visit some friends. That means they will be out of London for about four weeks. You must not lose contact with them during this period. I want you to arrange to meet them at least once during their stay in the Birmingham area.'

'Any particular date?' Tonya asked.

'Some time during their second week.'

They sat talking for nearly two hours. Timovitch, the working-class chauffeur in his poor looking suit and Fletcher the immaculately dressed businessman. Tonya only spoke when she had a question to ask, or if Timovitch asked her opinion, when her replies were always brief and to the point.

From the meeting Fletcher learned little about Timovitch's own work other than that he was living in a boarding house in the east end and was employed by one of the Ministries as a chauffeur. He was one of the masses. Who would suspect him of being a spy? But Fletcher didn't doubt that they would have friends in the civil service and one day soon Timovitch would be promoted to a car of importance, when he would become an obscure but sinister listener and observer.

At nine o'clock precisely Timovitch left, but not before arranging a further meeting, for two weeks later, when he expected Fletcher to have a comprehensive report for forwarding to Moscow. A simple signal was also agreed upon in case they wanted to contact him sooner. The track meetings at the Stadium were held two nights a week and Timovitch was a regular attender. If Fletcher was to park his car outside his office on the evening of a track meeting with an umbrella and hat lying on the rear seat, Timovitch would join them on the evening of the following track meeting.

Fletcher and Tonya left shortly after Timovitch. At the crossroads Fletcher caught a glimpse of him standing in the bus queue. He looked insignificant despite his large build. How many others were there like him, Fletcher wondered, living and operating in this country?

They drove to Redhill in silence, which was not uncommon. At first Fletcher used to wonder what Tonya was thinking about as she sat, poker-faced, staring out of the window, but he soon realised that she was such a mystery that it was futile to speculate. On this particular occasion Fletcher welcomed her silence. He was preoccupied with his own thoughts.

Timovitch's reference to Panama and Moscow's interest in the reaction of the British Government had suddenly changed the flavour and temper of his work. If Panama was about to become another international crisis area he didn't doubt but that the Communists had engineered the trouble. They never ceased planning and creating tension areas. It was part of their strategy.

But Fletcher was wondering whether Panama was not just the first step in hotting up the Cold War. Were they planning further confrontations? Further brinkmanship? Was that the reason for his time limit? And for his friendship with Sir

Joseph? Did they want someone close to the political heads when another area of international crisis was suddenly unleashed?

Fletcher was also curious to know how Timovitch was passing on the information to Moscow and getting his orders from them. He knew everything was being controlled by the spymasters in the Kremlin, even their own meetings. It was a weakness in their system, but nevertheless they maintained this rigid control. But it meant that someone had to operate a link with Moscow and he had a feeling that someone was neither Mikolyn nor Timovitch. Timovitch had been so well informed of Sir Joseph's movements as to suggest that someone close to Sir Joseph was in league with him and it was that someone who Fletcher thought was giving out the orders.

Fletcher didn't intend to waste any time in phoning Sir Joseph. With a fresh crisis about to make international news Sir Joseph could become even more difficult to contact. As for the outcome of his call, Fletcher had certain misgivings. His only hope was if Susan Manning had prepared the ground for him.

He telephoned Sir Joseph immediately they arrived at their house in Redhill and not only was Sir Joseph available, but he sounded remarkably friendly. He apologised for having been unable to attend the recent social functions Fletcher had arranged, but pressure of work at Westminster had kept him occupied. His wife and daughter, however, had enjoyed themselves and he was very grateful.

With such an admission Fletcher felt confident of success. He told Sir Joseph he had phoned to invite him out for lunch as he realised Sir Joseph had few evenings free. He offered no reason for the invitation, but had a number of fictitious business problems ready to use as a lever if necessary.

When Sir Joseph replied he again apologised, but as he was unable to spend very long over lunch he usually had it in his office or at the House of Commons. However, as an alternative, he suggested that Fletcher should have lunch with him at the Commons — a suggestion which Fletcher readily agreed to and arrangements were made for later that week.

The venue and the timing of their meeting could not have been bettered. If they were lunching in the home of politics then a general drift into that realm would not be unnatural and if anything broke within the next twenty four hours then when he met Sir Joseph it would still be very topical, but sufficient time would have lapsed to allow a more sober and realistic judgement on the issue.

Indeed, the arrangements were so perfect as to make Fletcher suspicious. Everything had fallen too neatly into place for his liking. Sir Joseph was being a little too co-operative. He began to wonder if the meeting was the result of Susan Manning's spade work after all, or if there wasn't some other reason for Sir Joseph's sudden availability.

Timovitch's forecast of the American move in Panama was well founded. The day after their meeting the newspaper headlines blazed the news in large black print. It swept all else off the front page.

The Americans made no attempt to conceal their reason for moving out of the Canal Zone and occupying the country. They were out to prevent another Cuba occurring in such a strategic position. But the subsequent reports of world opinion did not share the view that the uprising had been communist inspired.

The left-wing socialists bitterly attacked the Americans in Parliament and accused them of being frightened of their own shadow. Even the right-wing press was highly critical and was quick to remind the Americans of the Suez incident, where their lack of support still rankled. Once again the Americans were facing unpopular world opinion.

When Fletcher went to the House of Commons to join Sir Joseph for lunch the controversy was at its height. But, as he was escorted along the corridors by a uniformed attendant, the cloistered and almost monastic atmosphere, had a salutary, sobering and reassuring effect.

So it was in the huge, spacious, oak-panelled lounge into which he was taken, where in hushed tones matters of state were being discussed over aperitifs. The occupants of the room looked like a gathering of successful business men, but intermingled with them were also a number of overseas visitors in their own particular style of dress.

However, the rather sombre gathering of politicians didn't particularly impress Fletcher nor did the irony of his presence in such a building disturb him. To him all classes of society were vulnerable to penetration and once their particular mystic armour was removed they were all fundamentally the same. The political set at Westminster was no exception. But if the embellishments to his meeting with Sir Joseph didn't interest him the outcome certainly did. He was very curious to see what developed.

Sir Joseph was talking to two other men when he entered the room. He looked very much the statesman — tall, erect and dignified. The two men with him were a contrast. One was a severe-looking man with pointed features and a beak-like nose. He was a man in his late fifties, tall with thinning hair and dressed immaculately in the uniform of a civil servant — dark jacket and striped trousers. The other man was much younger.

He was of medium build, dapper and with jet black hair and a handsome face.

Sir Joseph greeted Fletcher warmly and introduced him to the two men as a friend. In the terms of his introduction Fletcher realised the value of his rather mundane role. He was so isolated from politics that he could be accepted on face value. For a while he had doubted the wisdom of the Soviets in creating the role so divorced from Westminster, but he had been looking at it from the point of view of establishing a common bond with Sir Joseph. However, he now realised the value of his isolation. If he had any trace of political affiliations or connections Sir Joseph would have dropped him like a hot brick, but in his present position he could be accepted and introduced at will without fear of any incriminations.

The tall man was introduced as a Mister Prentice and Fletcher soon gathered he was a senior official in Sir Joseph's department. The other man was called Langford, a name Fletcher knew. He was an M.P., a junior secretary under Sir Joseph and a man who was constantly being referred to in the popular press as an up and coming politician.

After the introductions and a brief exchange of general conversation the two men politely took their leave.

Their departure only just preceded the arrival of Susan Manning. Fletcher had not expected her joining them, but he quickly realised it was to his advantage. Timovitch expected him at the Mannings' cocktail party which was being held the following Sunday and as Tonya had pointed out Susan Manning was the most likely member of the family to do the inviting.

She came over to them smiling and gave her father an affectionate kiss.

'I am pleased frosty face is not lunching with us,' she said laughingly.

Sir Joseph frowned.

'I wish you wouldn't call him that, dear,' he said.

'Oh, Father, don't worry. He will never know and he is an old fusspot.'

Fletcher knew who they were referring to, but took the opportunity to find out more about the man.

'And who is frosty face?' he asked.

She gave him a mocked look of surprise.

'Why, Mr Prentice, of course,' she said and added secretively, 'he runs the department.' She turned to her father. 'Doesn't he, dear?'

'He is extremely capable and efficient,' Sir Joseph said and indicated that the subject was closed. He ordered drinks and they stood and talked. Their conversation was innocent. Sir Joseph was more affable than he had ever been in Spain and appeared genuinely interested in Fletcher's welfare.

Susan Manning was in a gay mood, but whilst Fletcher enjoyed her company he began to wonder if her presence was not going to prove a drawback after all. The more pertinent topics which Fletcher had hoped to discuss with Sir Joseph were more suitable for a quiet man to man lunch.

However, they were about to go into the dining room when the tall languid figure of Phillip Buckley entered the room and the pattern of their lunch took a decidedly more interesting turn.

Buckley stood by the door, surveying the assembled company as if wondering which group he should join. Fletcher watched his act with interest, but was not surprised when he came over to them. Instinct told him there was more to Buckley than met the eye. It also told him that his arrival at that particular moment had not been coincidental, but carefully timed. What it didn't tell him was — why?

'Hullo, Sir Joseph and Susan,' Buckley said in his slow, cultured tones. He looked at Fletcher and held out his hand. 'Why of course,' he said. 'Mr Adams. How are you? Your holiday appears to have agreed with you.'

There was a double edge to his remark which Fletcher noted, but ignored. He accepted the man's handshake and made some suitable reply.

In Spain they had realised his value, but meeting him again in this particular room made it all the more obvious. He was almost part of the constitution and as the watchdog of the press his eyes and ears would miss nothing.

Susan Manning was pleased to see him and showed it. Fletcher was not surprised. In looks Buckley was quite handsome with lean, pointed features and long fair hair and his tall, thin build gave him the appearance of a guards officer — a role which would have suited his sophisticated manner.

'Are you having lunch?' he asked.

'Yes,' Sir Joseph replied, 'come and join us.'

'Well, so long as I am not intruding.'

His remark had been addressed to Sir Joseph, but he was looking straight at Fletcher. Fletcher held his gaze.

'Of course not, Phillip,' Sir Joseph muttered.

'But you must promise not to discuss politics,' Susan Manning added.

'My dear girl, I really must. How else can I make my living? Besides, they expect it of me, otherwise I wouldn't get so many invitations to lunch.' He turned to Fletcher. 'I hope I won't bore you,' he said.

Again their eyes met.

'On the contrary,' Fletcher said. 'I shall find it stimulating.'

In the dining room Buckley was true to his word and it wasn't long before he was asking the questions Fletcher would have asked himself. It was almost as if he had been a witness at Fletcher's meeting with Timovitch.

Sir Joseph answered Buckley's questions freely and strongly criticised the Americans for exceeding the limits of their authority. Fletcher was quite content to remain the silent listener, but Susan Manning eventually tired of the political discussions.

'Father, please,' she said.

'Sorry, dear,' Sir Joseph muttered apologetically.

Buckley drifted into general conversation, unabashed.

'Are you contemplating any further holidays?' he asked Fletcher.

''Fraid not,' Fletcher replied. 'Maybe later in the year.'

'How about you, Phillip?' Susan Manning asked.

Buckley found as much pleasure talking about himself as he did about politics.

'Well, as a matter of fact, I am,' he said. 'I am off to the Continent for a couple of weeks or so.'

'Anywhere special?' Fletcher asked.

'No, just touring about. Probably spend a bit of time in Germany and Austria. I have one or two hotels booked, but I like to leave a few days in between each booking so that I can drift about.'

'Sounds marvellous,' Susan Manning said enthusiastically.

Buckley agreed. 'Yes, it does. Actually, what I do is give the travel agency the names of a few places where I want to stay and the dates and they do the rest. They are very good.'

Fletcher waited and allowed Susan Manning to ask the obvious.

'Which agency is it?'

'The Continental Travel Agency.'

Fletcher's pulse quickened. It was too much of a coincidence. He purposely didn't look at Buckley, but he felt Buckley was watching him closely.

'I can recommend them, also,' Fletcher remarked casually. 'They fixed up our holiday in Spain.'

'Oh, did they?' Buckley asked deeply interested.

'Isn't that who we used, my dear?' Sir Joseph asked.

'So it is,' Susan Manning said enthusiastically. 'What a small world.'

Perhaps not so small if the truth was really known, Fletcher thought.

'I appear to have made a popular choice,' Buckley remarked dryly.

The matter passed over, but it gave Fletcher food for thought. Sir Joseph's booking through the Continental Travel Agency could have been innocent. As for Buckley, Fletcher was not so sure. Somehow the agency was connected to the Soviet spy network. Was Buckley also?

For a while they discussed the Mannings' movements during the coming Parliamentary recess and the information Timovitch had given Fletcher was accurate to a detail.

During the lunch Fletcher also learned about Mikolyn's progress. With a wily smile Susan Manning remarked that he was a persistent sort of man. Both Sir Joseph and Buckley took a surprised interest in her remark and Fletcher noticed Sir Joseph's face cloud over.

'I do wish you wouldn't go out with so many different men,' he said.

Again his daughter scolded him affectionately.

'Oh, Father, don't be so concerned. Besides, Gary is a friend of Paul's.'

'The son of a business contact, to be precise,' Fletcher explained.

Sir Joseph mumbled a half-hearted apology, but he was obviously displeased at his daughter's actions. Buckley's interest had not been verbal, but Fletcher noticed he was taking in all the details despite his apparent languid appearance.

The remainder of the lunch passed without incident, but unfortunately Sir Joseph had to leave them to their coffee to attend to some business before going to the House. Before he left, however, Fletcher had got his agreement to an evening playing bridge in the not too distant future. But there had been no invitation to his cocktail party the following Sunday or any suggestion of a get-together in Birmingham.

Fletcher was a little concerned. Timovitch wanted him at that party and he didn't want to fail him, otherwise their spymasters might devise some other devilish scheme to achieve their object — a scheme which might not include Fletcher.

He waited patiently for an opportunity to make a move, but it was not until they were all leaving that Buckley presented the opening he had been waiting for.

'You must both have lunch with me some time,' he said.

Fletcher didn't hesitate.

'I'd love to,' he said, 'but look here — Susan is off to Birmingham soon so why don't you both come over for lunch on Sunday and I'll invite Vincent as well.'

Before Buckley had an opportunity to accept, Susan Manning intervened.

'Oh, I am sorry, Paul,' she said, 'but father is having several of his business friends for cocktails and I'm afraid I'll have to help.'

'That's a pity,' Fletcher agreed.

Fortunately Buckley didn't let the matter rest there. He was deeply concerned.

'But Susan, dear, you never mentioned this and you know how I rely on such functions. Or were you not going to invite me for some reason or other?'

'Oh, Phillip, don't be like that. As a matter of fact father only mentioned it to me this morning. Of course you must come, or you'll start imagining all sorts of political intrigue.'

Having opened the door to Buckley she had placed herself at a disadvantage. After a short delicate pause she turned to Fletcher and said: 'Why don't you come over as well, Paul? With Jane. I'm afraid it will be rather dreary, but you are very welcome.'

It was a half-hearted invitation meant to give him the opportunity of declining. Fletcher had no such intention, but he wanted Susan Manning to be more pressing. He didn't want to appear too eager in front of Buckley. But Buckley solved the problem for him.

'Yes, old man,' he said enthusiastically, 'bring your charming wife and keep me company. I'm sure you won't find it half so dreary as Susan imagines.'

Fletcher didn't hesitate to settle the matter.

'Thanks a lot,' he said. 'We would love to come.'

'That's agreed then,' Buckley drawled. 'We all meet for cocktails next Sunday at eleven.'

He smiled as he spoke, but there was something in his manner which made their next meeting seem more like the continuation of an affray rather than a social gathering.

Chapter Eleven

The invitation to the cocktail party was of immense value to Fletcher and Tonya. It presented them as friends of the Mannings and gave them an opportunity to make further political contacts. But Fletcher also had another reason for wanting to be present. If Sir Joseph wasn't giving the Soviets details of his movements himself, someone close to the man was, and unless Fletcher was mistaken that someone would be at the cocktail party.

When they arrived at the Mannings the following Sunday a large number of guests were already present. Sir Joseph and Lady Manning greeted them warmly and handed them over to Susan. As she attended to their drinks Fletcher glanced around the room.

Buckley was there, his tall figure bent over a cocktail glass in the typical pose of a social habituate. He was talking to two men and Fletcher immediately recognised them as the men he had been introduced to in the House of Commons — Langford and Prentice. They were accompanied by their wives and it wasn't difficult for Fletcher to pair them off. One of the women was attractive and smartly dressed, whilst the other was a rather drab looking person. Not only did Langford have the personal attributes to succeed, he also had the right type of wife to help him.

Fletcher wondered about the two men. They both worked very closely with Sir Joseph — Prentice on the administration side and Langford on the political — they would both be well informed of Sir Joseph's movements — especially Langford.

He decided they were both worthy of further attention.

The other guests were a mixed selection of men and women of varying ages, but Fletcher noted with satisfaction that the white haired Davies was present — the man Timovitch had told him to meet.

As Susan returned with their drinks Buckley came over to them. He acknowledged Fletcher with a nod of his head and addressed himself to Tonya.

'Hullo, Mrs Adams, how nice to see you again,' he said. 'Let me introduce you to some of the guests.'

He exchanged glances with Fletcher and there was something in his look which both irritated and puzzled Fletcher. His expression had been faintly mocking, rather like a child who knew a secret, but wasn't going to tell. He ushered Tonya over to the group he had just left and Fletcher followed behind. Unfortunately the Langfords had moved on, leaving only the stern-faced civil servant and his wife.

Buckley made the necessary introductions and like a man well accustomed to such functions kept the conversation alive.

Prentice, with his poker-like features, was crisp and unforthcoming with his conversation. He spoke only when Buckley or Fletcher addressed him directly and his replies gave the impression that he studied his words carefully before he spoke. He was devoid of any apparent pleasing personality and Fletcher could only assume that his administrative ability more than made up for his other shortcomings.

His wife was equally unattractive and even more difficult to converse with. She was like a woman who had all her enthusiasm and interests drained out of her by the constant presence of her puritanical husband.

Tonya, however, gradually eased her out of the group and talked to her by herself. A move which Fletcher would have applauded if their visit had been purely social, but under the present circumstances he considered it a waste of time. Even with Prentice, himself, he was beginning to question the merits of prolonging their conversation. It was not until he casually asked Prentice what he intended to do during the Parliamentary recess that anything of value came out of their talks.

His question was surprisingly seized upon by Buckley.

'Oh, this is his golden opportunity,' Buckley said with great delight. 'The department can now get on with its work without any interference. Isn't that so, Prentice?'

'We carry on as usual.'

'Without hindrance,' Buckley persisted.

'The politicians govern and we administer,' Prentice remarked dryly.

'When do you take your leave?' Fletcher asked.

Prentice studied his glass as if looking into a crystal ball.

'I hope to get away towards the end of August.'

'Hope?' Buckley quickly asked. 'Is this American business as serious as that?'

'It was purely a figure of speech,' Prentice said slowly, 'but one never knows these days.'

It was a diplomatic answer but not very convincing.

'I understand the Minister is staying in town,' Buckley remarked.

'So I believe,' Prentice said, 'but doesn't he always?'

'I wouldn't know, but Sir Joseph is not travelling far. It would appear as if they are standing by.'

Again Prentice studied his glass.

'It is as well to take precautions,' he said finally.

Fletcher didn't add any further fuel to their particular topic. He had learned quite a lot from the few remarks and didn't want to appear over inquisitive. As it was he was both surprised by Buckley's rather direct questions and Prentice's vague, but decidedly pointed, replies. But then they weren't to know what Tonya or Fletcher were doing — or did they?

'Where do you hope to get to?' Fletcher asked.

As if relieved by the change of topic Prentice replied almost immediately.

'The Adriatic Coast,' he said. 'We have gone there for the past two years.'

It was not where Fletcher would have guessed. Somehow he didn't quite get the picture of Prentice basking in the sun. But he was not particularly interested in Prentice's movements and when Buckley embarked upon a long tirade on the merits of various continental resorts he became restless. Timovitch had wanted him there to meet people, not to listen to the loquacious Buckley and one of those people, Hugh Davies, had apparently got tired of standing and was sitting by himself on a window seat.

He caught Tonya's eyes and gave her the signal that he was on the move. When Susan Manning rejoined them Fletcher engaged her in conversation, whilst Tonya eased herself back into the group.

After a short while Fletcher casually remarked: 'Isn't that Hugh Davies over there?'

'Yes, that's right,' Susan Manning replied. 'Have you met him?'

'No, but I would like to.'

'Come along then, I will introduce you.'

She took hold of his arm and led him across the room to where the venerable looking politician was sitting.

'Mr Davies,' she said eagerly, 'I would like you to meet a friend of mine.'

Davies gave her a warm smile and stood up. She made the necessary introductions and the two men shook hands.

'Let me get you another drink,' Susan Manning said. She took Davies' glass and left them.

'Do you mind if we sit?' Davies asked.

'Certainly not.'

Fletcher joined Davies on the bench seat. As he did so he caught Langford watching him from across the room. He held his gaze and Langford smiled. But Langford had not been looking at him for a sign of recognition. His expression had been one of curiosity. Fletcher wondered why?

Undaunted, he set about cultivating Davies. It wasn't difficult. Davies had an easy, jovial manner and appeared to welcome his company. He talked freely about the many people he had met and of his experiences during his long service in politics and Fletcher wondered why a man so gregarious in nature and almost celestial in appearance had attracted the attention of Moscow. He appeared to epitomise the respectable, dedicated socialist politician.

But Fletcher knew Moscow didn't bandy names around lightly, or make a move without an aim in view. There was some reason, hidden to Fletcher, why he had been told to meet this man.

As their conversation prolonged Fletcher noticed Davies become more friendly. He laughed heartily at his own anecdotes and his hand occasionally rested on Fletcher's shoulder. To the guests who often glanced in their direction it would appear they were close friends. Was Davies doing this on purpose? he wondered. Was this why Timovitch had told him to make his acquaintance? Was it all part of a scheme to promote Fletcher in front of Sir Joseph's political friends? Was

Davies, in fact, something other than a pleasant, engaging old man of the Socialist Party?

A lull in the general hub of conversation made Fletcher take notice. All eyes were turned to the entrance to the lounge where Sir Joseph and his wife were greeting some further guests. The quick murmur that passed around the groups indicated they were guests of importance. There was no introductions made or were necessary — it was the Minister and his party.

The Minister and his wife stood talking to Sir Joseph and Lady Manning, but after a short while Lady Manning took the Minister's wife over to a corner group where she was evidently known. Sir Joseph and the Minister were then joined by Langford and on the fringe was Prentice waiting to be summoned. Fletcher saw the Minister give him the signal and Prentice also joined the rather serious looking party.

Fletcher took up his conversation again with Davies, but he noticed that the man's eyes kept a close watch on the Minister's actions. When the Minister and his party left the room, apparently to discuss business in privacy, Davies very politely excused himself and joined them. A privilege, which Fletcher assumed, the old man enjoyed through his long service to the party.

Fletcher decided to take the opportunity to meet the other guests and began to circulate. He could not have picked a more ideal moment. The alcohol was beginning to take effect and reserves were beginning to drop. Discussions and arguments flowed uninhibited.

When the Minister and his party returned to the lounge he only remained long enough to collect his wife before leaving. There had been no social intercourse — it had been a working party. Davies did not reappear and Langford and Prentice also soon departed. Fletcher rejoined Tonya and Buckley until the opportunity presented itself for them to leave.

Fletcher and Sir Joseph shook hands and Lady Manning said she was pleased they had come and hoped they hadn't found the party boring. Tonya ridiculed the suggestion and continued to act her part superbly even to the perfunctory embrace with Lady Manning as they departed.

Susan Manning accompanied them to their car and promised to phone them immediately she returned. She was the most friendly and most co-operative member of the family. Without her their work would have been an uphill battle.

On their journey back to Redhill they relaxed and compared notes.

Tonya had spent most of the morning talking to Buckley and it had been a fruitful discussion. He had given her the background of practically everyone in the room. She had learned more than Fletcher with less effort.

On the international front they agreed that the American intervention in Panama had upset many members of the British Government, including Sir Joseph and despite the Prime Minister's efforts to minimise their differences the relations between the two countries were becoming rather strained. Britain was also watching the situation very closely for fear of similar trouble in the neighbouring British Guiana where the neo-communist party was at present in opposition, but where a further call on the British Army would tax her resources to the limit.

They also discussed their findings on other political matters, mainly concerned with domestic affairs and assessed the value to the communist party of the various guests in the room.

Fletcher also had other problems which he kept to himself. For him there were three major imponderables. Why was

Moscow so interested in Sir Joseph? Who was supplying them with all the information about his movements? — and where was British Security?

There was a leak at the top. British Intelligence knew that and so did certain members of the Government — very few. Was Sir Joseph that leak? Was that why he was being cultivated? Was it so that at the right moment he could pass on further secrets?

Their friendship had been achieved without any great difficulty. A little slow at first, but it certainly had happened. Sir Joseph could well have been playing it clever, appearing reticent and unable to attend social engagements, but always making sure his wife and daughter did. He could certainly be more than he appeared.

Lady Manning and her daughter, Susan, were also strong suspects. Both had full knowledge of all Sir Joseph's movements. Both were very eager to share Tonya and Fletcher's company and both were highly intelligent.

Lady Manning was the more likely suspect than her daughter, because of her age, experience and connections. Fletcher placed her high on the list. Underneath he put Buckley. His contacts, his privileged position, his friendship with Sir Joseph could all have been put to the cause of Moscow. Buckley had helped Fletcher both at the lunch and the cocktail party. But for his help they would not have ever been invited to the cocktail party. Had that been accidental or intentional? And his developing friendship with Tonya was suspicious.

But Fletcher realised that what he attributed to the cause of Russian Intelligence could also apply to British Intelligence. Buckley could also be a security agent helping Fletcher to establish himself. He was one or the other, he had been too helpful. Time would show which he was.

When they handed over their reports to Timovitch at their next meeting he accepted them without comment. Nor did he question them on their work. This puzzled Fletcher at first, but during the subsequent conversation his apparent lack of interest became obvious. He was already aware of their progress. Somebody else was keeping him informed.

With the Mannings out of town for a few weeks Fletcher and Tonya's orders were simply to keep the office functioning and to tour around the countryside making contacts. The normal everyday routine of observation and talent spotting.

The next meeting with Timovitch was delayed until early September, but in case an emergency meeting was required they agreed upon a simple coded system of passing messages via the advertisement column of an evening newspaper. As Timovitch had acquired a motorcycle, future meetings were to take place in the country and a series of rendezvous were arranged at isolated locations.

The following weeks were a trial of Fletcher's patience. He disliked the bustle and the crowd of the city at the height of the summer. The daily trips to the office he found boring and what little business did filter through was speedily dealt with by Tonya.

Her thoroughness and efficiency also irritated him. She never made a mistake, she never relaxed, not even in their home and as a result neither could he. But there were times when it was obvious she was also feeling the strain of their nebulous existence.

During this waiting period Fletcher kept a close watch on the international scene. The Americans' actions were still provoking criticism and despite the efforts of the British Government to minimise the issue, there were many signs that the cordial relations between the two countries were becoming strained. The Russians, however, were playing the docile bear, righteously insisting that the medium of the United Nations be used to settle the dispute. A cry which found a lot of support in the press.

When the Mannings returned to London from their holiday Susan Manning did not phone them as she had promised and when they did meet her again her attitude gave them cause for concern. She was reserved and quiet, almost like a stranger. It was apparent that something was worrying her and Fletcher wondered whether Mikolyn had fouled it up. Fortunately Sir Joseph and Lady Manning were more sociable.

Towards the end of September, however, events took an unexpected turn. No longer did it become a matter of social exchanges. The gloves came off and the iron fists were bared. It became a deadly serious business.

Chapter Twelve

'That's grand. Eight-thirty in the cocktail bar, tomorrow evening.'

Fletcher confirmed the arrangements and thoughtfully replaced the phone on the receiver. The person at the other end of the line had been Buckley — Buckley who they had not seen or heard from since the cocktail party at the Mannings. Nor had they seen any of his articles in the press. The invitation had come out of the blue.

He passed on the message to Tonya. Buckley wanted them to join him for a small dinner party he was giving at the Bridge Inn in Thorpe, the following evening. The Langfords were also invited and so were two other guests whose names had not been mentioned.

Tonya welcomed the invitation and Fletcher wondered if she had any personal feelings for being pleased. He was also pleased, but for a different reason. Buckley puzzled him and Langford interested him. The two together should make an interesting evening.

When they arrived at the Bridge Inn the following evening it was already dark. Fletcher parked the car and with Tonya walked across the illuminated gravel car park.

Casually, he scanned the parked cars and picked out Buckley's. Alongside it stood a highly polished fawn saloon. His pulse quickened and he stopped dead in his tracks. The fawn saloon was a Rover. And the registration number was familiar.

Tonya turned to see what was delaying him.

'That car!' he said in an urgent whisper.

She looked at the Rover.

'Smith's?' she asked almost unbelievingly.

'Same registration number,' he whispered, 'and with the G.B. plate.'

Could it really be them? he wondered. Were they in the hotel? He had automatically looked at the registration number of every fawn Rover saloon he had seen, but he had never really expected to come across the Smiths again. Yet here was the same type of car and the same registration number.

He took hold of Tonya's arm.

'Come on,' he said, 'let's see who is inside.'

When they entered the hotel lounge, they saw Buckley straight away. He was standing at the entrance to the cocktail bar, glass in hand, talking to his other guests who were hidden by a glass screen. He immediately came over to them.

'Come and meet two friends of mine,' he said and ushered them into the small cocktail bar. Again Fletcher's pulse quickened, but he knew what to expect. Buckley stood to one side and as they entered the room they came face to face with the Smiths.

But if Buckley expected any reaction from Fletcher or Tonya, he was disappointed. They had been pre-warned by the car. If the Smiths were taken by surprise they covered up remarkably well, except that Smith got off his stool rather too quickly and spilt part of his drink. Mrs Smith, however, remained seated and just smiled.

There was a fractional pause before Buckley made the necessary introductions. A pause long enough for Buckley to see if any perceivable sign of recognition took place between the two couples. But the Smiths, like Fletcher and Tonya, gave no such sign.

'This is Mr and Mrs Grant,' Buckley said introducing the Smiths.

'Charles and Judy, please, Phillip,' Mrs Smith said.

'Of course, Judy dear and this is Paul and Jane Adams.'

They exchanged handshakes and Buckley ordered further drinks. The fact that the Smiths had a different name did not surprise Fletcher, but their presence did. There had been not the slightest hint of them operating in England, but now he knew who Timovitch was passing on their reports to and who was giving him his orders from Moscow.

'I thought you may have all known each other,' Buckley remarked.

'Why is that, Phillip?' Tonya asked in the haughty, sophisticated tone she had perfected.

'Yes, why is that, old boy?' Smith added.

'They are clients of yours,' Buckley said to Smith. He passed the drinks around and turned to Tonya. 'I understand you used the services of the Continental Travel Agency when you visited Spain. Well, Charles and Judy are the Continental Travel Agency.'

The Continental Travel Agency! My God! Fletcher thought. What an ideal set up. It could explain their frequent trips to the Continent. Trips that allowed them to stop behind the iron curtain. And their courier in Spain.

He would well imagine how popular Buckley was with them at that precise moment.

'Oh dear, I do hope you have no complaints,' Mrs Smith said with a nervous laugh. 'I do get so worried when I meet any of Charles's clients.'

'On the contrary,' Fletcher said, 'your firm gave us excellent service.'

'We arranged our holiday through your office in the Strand,' Tonya explained.

'That is why we never met,' Smith said. 'Our head office is in Wembley. We find it more convenient than being in the City. Where did you get to in Spain?'

They had little opportunity, however, to discuss their holiday in Spain, as they were joined by the Langfords. Again, Buckley waited that fraction of a second before making the necessary introductions, but again there was no sign of recognition from the Smiths.

The Langfords presented an entirely different picture to the Smiths. Langford was suave, confident and highly intelligent and his wife was equally confident and extremely attractive. They were an accomplished couple who soon made their presence felt.

But as they stood and talked it became apparent to Fletcher that not only did Langford interest him, but he in turn also interested Langford. In a roundabout way Langford questioned him about his friendship with Sir Joseph and became extremely interested in their business. It was almost as if he were storing up a number of details which he could later check.

Mrs Smith was acting the same foppish part she had played when Fletcher had first met her, whilst her husband tried hard to compete with Langford. It was a strange cocktail Buckley had mixed and Fletcher wondered if he realised just how potent he had made it.

It was obvious now to Fletcher which camp Buckley belonged to. If he had been working for the Soviets he would never have got the Smiths out into the open. Buckley was part of British Security. Somewhere he had come across the Smiths. Somehow he had connected them with the spy ring. But why had he brought them face to face with Fletcher? Why had he been looking for some sign of recognition? It was a dangerous move. He had put the Smiths on the stage. Something they had never intended.

And where did the Langfords fit into the plot? Why were they here? Had they been invited to make the party appear respectable? Or were they also playing a double role? Was Buckley trying to tell him something?

Inwardly, he cursed Buckley for his blundering. If British Security wanted to contact him or help him there were other less dangerous ways of doing it. They could have arranged a chance meeting with him instead of trying to be so damned clever. A sudden thought occurred to him. Perhaps Buckley didn't know who Fletcher really was. Perhaps British Security were asleep after all. But he recalled how Buckley had helped him at the lunch and it gave him hope.

The evening progressed in the manner the Smiths had shown them during their training and Fletcher couldn't help admire Tonya's masterly performance. If the Smiths were looking for anything to salvage from the evening it was the consolation of knowing their weeks of patient training had produced the desired result.

Tonya did not have the striking beauty of Langford's wife, but with her long, dark brown hair and dark eyes, she was nevertheless very attractive and in company she had a very engaging personality. It was not surprising that Buckley was attracted to her and if Fletcher had not known her for what she really was their relationship could also have been different.

Her acting, however, also made him wonder what the rest were really thinking as they went through the motions of appearing to enjoy the evening.

Was Langford, for instance, so much at ease, so entertaining and so in command of the situation as he appeared? Did his wife really find Smith so amusing? Or were they both as inwardly concerned as he knew the Smiths were?

The Smiths tried hard, but they slipped during the meal. They could control their outward emotions, but not their digestive system. The dinner, excellent though it was, was a failure as far as the Smiths were concerned. Mrs Smith ate very little and her husband failed miserably at the second course. In an endeavour to make up for his shortcomings he overacted and talked too much. By the close of the evening it was obvious to Fletcher that Smith was a badly shaken man. It was also obvious that there would be repercussions.

On their return to Redhill Tonya refused to discuss either Buckley or the Smiths. Like an obedient servant she was prepared to leave such matters to her masters in Moscow.

But Fletcher felt there was also another reason for her silence. So far they had had it all their own way, but now Buckley had put a spoke in their wheels. Beneath her hard crusted exterior she was worried. Detection had become a possibility and for the first time since the beginning of their relationship he felt more kindly disposed towards her.

Chapter Thirteen

Two days later came the reaction Fletcher had been expecting. Mikolyn was again the medium and he phoned and invited them to join him the following afternoon, a Saturday, on a sightseeing tour of the city.

It was only their third meeting with Mikolyn and each one had been for a purpose. On this occasion the sightseeing was purely a foil, a trip around the city to make absolutely certain they were not being tailed. They motored from place to place in Fletcher's Daimler until Mikolyn was satisfied there was not the slightest suggestion that anyone was interested in their movements.

When they abandoned their sightseeing, he directed them out of the city into Wembley. They parked the car on a vacant plot at the side of a large multiple store and for a few moments sat smoking.

From the car park they strolled into the store and spent a short while examining the various counters. When they left the store it was by a rear door which opened on to a narrow lane. In the lane was a man washing a car.

Mikolyn hesitated, but when the man turned his back on them he quickly ushered them into the backyard of the building opposite. Without further delay he led them up a steel fire escape ladder and into a small room, where the Smiths and Timovitch were sitting waiting for them.

The room was furnished only with the bare essentials to indicate that it was used as an office, but there was nothing which gave any indication as to the nature of the business.

However, there was a distinct smell of soap powder.

But it was not a social visit. It was a council of war and Mrs Smith, or Grant as she was really called, took the chair. Like the time before in their bungalow, when Fletcher had been given his orders, Mrs Smith again became the stern faced agent and her husband watched from the sideline.

'You were not followed? You are certain?' she asked Mikolyn.

'Certain,' Mikolyn replied.

'Good,' Mrs Smith said.

She looked at them all individually, but when she spoke she addressed them collectively.

'I want to know every detail about your contact with Buckley.' She almost spat out his name. 'Everything.' She turned to Fletcher. 'You first.'

Fletcher related his encounter with Buckley in Spain, their lunch together with Sir Joseph and their conversation at the cocktail party.

Throughout, Mrs Smith kept interrupting him with questions. Who was with him? Who did he talk to? What did he say? What did he do? When he came to the dinner she made him go over his story a second time. Had he mentioned their name? Who had he said was going to join them? Did they have any warning who it would be? Did the Smiths show any sign of surprise? Did they see anyone watching them?

When she had drained Fletcher she started on Tonya and got her views.

But Fletcher and Tonya were not the only ones Buckley had become acquainted with. Both Mikolyn and Timovitch knew him.

Fletcher listened as eagerly as the Smiths as Mikolyn explained his contact.

'I first met him at Sir Joseph's home. I had taken Susan Manning out for dinner and when we returned he was talking to Sir Joseph in the lounge.'

He had also met him on other occasions, but always when he had been in the company of Susan Manning. Once they had come across him in a restaurant where they were having lunch, but the other occasions had always been at Sir Joseph's home. It was obvious that Buckley was giving Sir Joseph a lot of attention. Fletcher wondered why.

Timovitch's report was equally interesting and very illuminating.

'He has been in my car on four occasions,' he explained. 'On each of these occasions I have been driving Mr Langford. The first time was on July 17th when I drove Langford from Whitehall to his home in Kent. The second was when I drove Langford and Buckley to the Services Club in the Strand. It was on the afternoon of July 30th. The last two occasions were both this week when I drove them to Langford's home, last Tuesday and Wednesday evening.'

Fletcher listened incredulously. Timovitch, the ordinary looking man with the least spectacular role, had managed to get himself into a position of unusual advantage — chauffeur to Langford, the up and coming politician, who could one day be the Minister himself. The man who was already knocking on Sir Joseph's door. Timovitch had done very well, but he could not have done it by himself. There must be friends helping him from the inside. And why Langford? Was that also for a reason?

'Wednesday was the evening of the dinner party,' Mrs Smith said abruptly. 'What was discussed?'

Timovitch remembered their conversation well. He had been thoroughly trained. But their conversation had been on general

131

topics and nothing which could help Mrs Smith. She questioned him about the other journeys, but again their conversation had been innocent. Whatever they were planning to discuss they had left until they reached their destination.

Fletcher was beginning to see what Buckley was up to. He was putting the rule over the top echelon. He was working from the inside. Even the Minister would not have escaped his microscopic eye. If only he had not attempted to bring the outside and inside forces together.

When Mrs Smith had finished questioning Timovitch she considered the matter silently for a brief moment and then said: 'Buckley is working for British Security. I have been aware of this for some time, but he has done nothing which would jeopardise our plans. Not until a few days ago. Now he has become very dangerous. Not only does he suspect my husband and me, but he is also getting too close to a friend of our cause. A person who must be protected at all costs.' She repeated the words: 'At all costs!'

No one spoke as she paused. The room was deadly quiet.

Fletcher waited eagerly for her to continue. Someone was a Red, a fellow traveller, a dupe. This was what he had been told, but here was Mrs Smith spelling it out for him. If only she would name the person his work would be finished. Who was it? Who? Was it Sir Joseph?

'I have made plans to deal with Buckley,' she said in a tone which completely shred her of any feminine charm. 'You will each be told what you must do and there must be no mistakes.'

It was Buckley's death warrant. She was planning to kill him! Fletcher felt sick inside. What could he do? If he made one wrong move it could foul up all his work.

'If we deal with Buckley,' he said cautiously, 'won't that confirm their suspicions?'

She looked at him coldly.

'It will give us time,' she said, 'and we don't need much.'

He said no more. In questioning her decision he had already gone too far. To have said more would have made her suspicious.

She gave a signal to her husband who stood up and asked Timovitch and Mikolyn to join him next door for a drink. It left Fletcher and Tonya alone in the room with his wife. She looked at Fletcher.

'I want you to phone Buckley and arrange to meet him at the Bridge Inn on Monday evening at eight-thirty precisely. You can use the public phone in the room downstairs. My husband will take you to it. You can suggest to Buckley that you want to have a talk with him about things of mutual interest. I leave it to you what you say, so long as you can get him there. He does not suspect you, yet.'

'What if he is unable to make it Monday evening?'

'If you make it sound sufficiently interesting he will be there, but if necessary make it the following evening.'

'Do I book a table for dinner in advance?'

'No. It will not be necessary.'

She didn't enlarge upon her statement, but Fletcher took it she was not referring to the popularity of the hotel.

'Do I turn up at the Bridge Inn?' Fletcher persisted.

'Yes, but do not expose yourself if Buckley is not there.'

Fletcher understood the inference. Somewhere between his home and the Bridge Inn, Buckley was going to be 'dealt with'.

'One further point,' Mrs Smith said. 'Just in case Buckley should cancel the meeting, phone the Travel Agency office in the Strand at precisely four-thirty on Monday afternoon. Use a public phone box. If the arrangements stand ask the girl who will answer the phone what the time of departure is for Mrs

Adams' flight to Paris on Friday evening. If the meeting has been cancelled for that evening tell the girl you wish to cancel Mrs Adams' flight to Paris scheduled for Friday evening. Phone each day at four-thirty with one of those messages. However, I expect you to be able to get him there on Monday.'

'What do I do?' Tonya asked.

'Nothing,' Mrs Smith replied. 'You remain at your house in Redhill all evening and if necessary you can swear that your husband was there also.'

Thank God for that, Fletcher thought. At least he would be by himself. It gave him a fighting chance to somehow help Buckley.

'I will get my husband to take you to the public telephone. If Buckley is not available keep phoning until you contact him. But use a public box. We must be extra cautious from now on. Only use your own phone if the call is completely innocent.'

'I understand.'

'That is all, then. After your call you can leave with Vincent.'

She opened a drawer and produced two small automatic pistols and two packages of cartridges. She handed one of each to Fletcher and Tonya. Fletcher checked his weapon to make sure that it wasn't loaded and put it in his pocket.

'What about further meetings?' he asked.

'Carry on as before. Our plans are not altered.'

She pressed a button on her desk and her husband rejoined them. She explained what Fletcher had to do and he took charge of them.

As they followed him out of the room Mikolyn was called in to receive his orders, but Timovitch remained in the other room. Only the Smiths knew what each one was doing. Fletcher wondered who was to be the assassin.

Smith led them along a narrow corridor and down a flight of stairs into the room below. Fletcher had expected the room to be the front of one of the Travel Agency offices, but instead he was greeted with a room full of washing machines. It was a launderette. The Smiths had many strings to their bow.

In the corner was a public telephone and Fletcher was not surprised when Smith told him Buckley's telephone number and produced sufficient coins for a long talk.

Reluctantly Fletcher dialled the number. There was an even chance that Buckley was not at home, in which case he would have been free to make the arrangements himself without having Smith hovering in the background. But as if participating in the plot Buckley's affected drawl answered the call.

'This is Paul Adams,' Fletcher said.

'Oh, hullo old boy,' Buckley drawled.

'Phillip, I must see you. It is important.' Fletcher made it sound urgent. He wanted Buckley to realize there was something up, to put him on his guard.

There was a pause at the other end, then Buckley said: 'Well, I was just off for the weekend, but I can wait another hour or so. Come around now, I am on my own.'

'I can't Phillip, I am tied up all weekend. Could you meet me at the Bridge Inn on Monday evening? Let's say eight-thirty in the car park.'

Again there was a pause before Buckley replied. Fletcher cast a glance at Smith who nodded approvingly.

When Buckley did speak his manner had changed. His affected drawl was gone.

'Is this matter serious?' he asked.

'Yes,' Fletcher replied and added: 'very.'

Smith could not have overheard Buckley's question otherwise Fletcher would have tempered his reply, but it was the only way of putting it over to Buckley. He hoped Buckley would give him another opportunity to warn him.

'I think I understand,' Buckley said. 'I will be there. Monday at eight-thirty.'

There was nothing further Fletcher could say with his attentive audience.

'Good. See you Monday.'

He replaced the receiver.

'He will be there on Monday,' he said, but added, 'unless he phones in between.' He wanted to make sure he still had to use that public phone box to confirm their meeting.

They reported back to Mrs Smith who had finished briefing Mikolyn. She greeted the news with a contented nod of approval and Fletcher wondered which gave her the most satisfaction. The fact that her scheme was bearing fruit, or that Buckley's time was limited?

Soon after, Fletcher and Tonya left with Mikolyn. They returned to their car via the same devious route in which they had entered the launderette and with the same amount of caution. From Wembley they drove into the city and deposited Mikolyn close to Piccadilly.

Throughout their journey Fletcher's mind was preoccupied with the problem of Buckley. He had arranged for the man to go to his death. Somehow he had to warn him, or stop him from keeping the appointment.

But it was not so straightforward as it sounded. Fletcher was so close to his goal and the reward was of such national importance, that he could not afford to make a slip. If Buckley did not turn up the Smiths would want to know why? It would be obvious that someone had warned him and they wouldn't have to look very far. They were a small group.

During the ensuing weekend he mentally wrestled with the problem and finally made a decision. If Tonya gave him the opportunity, he would contact the police and get them to pass on a message to British Security to warn Buckley of the danger. If Buckley was a British agent, he would get the message. If he wasn't, nothing would be lost, the message would not get past British Security.

But during the weekend Tonya never let him out of her sight. She appeared to cling to him like a leech and by the Sunday evening he gave up all hope of contacting the police. The following day, he knew, would be the same. The only opportunity he was going to get was when he phoned the Smiths at four-thirty in the afternoon and by then it would probably be too late to get the message through the necessary channels.

But at four-thirty there was nothing stopping him speaking to Buckley himself. He decided he would phone Buckley when he phoned the Smiths and warn him of the danger, but the meeting would still have to take place. If for some reason he couldn't get hold of Buckley he would get a message to him bringing their meeting forward by one hour. This would mean that Buckley would arrive at the Bridge Inn before the assassin was ready for him. In either case suspicion would not necessarily be put on Fletcher.

On the Monday morning, before he drove into the city, he made certain two of the leads from the distributor head of the car were disconnected. Consequently, the engine did not give its best performance and it was apparent, even to Tonya, that it needed attention.

He took the car to a garage near their office and saw the foreman in charge in the privacy of his workshop. After a brief discussion with him, he returned to Tonya and presented her with the facts. The car could be repaired, but it would not be finished before seven o'clock that evening. An arrangement which Fletcher had carefully manoeuvred.

Tonya agreed that they leave the car and she would return to Redhill by train. This meant that Fletcher could go directly to his meeting with Buckley at a time of his own choosing.

For the rest of the morning Fletcher sat in his office reading various newspapers, whilst Tonya attended to their business. This was their normal procedure, but on this occasion he read the newspapers with a feeling of mounting excitement. There were reports on unrest and student riots in Iran and Iraq. Two countries where a stable and friendly Government were essential to the British economy.

The whole of the Middle East had explosive potentials, Fletcher knew this only too well. He also knew the Russians had designs in Iran and were eager to get a foothold amongst the Arab States.

Not only did the reports of the rioting give Fletcher cause for concern, but also the fact that they were taking place at a time when the Egyptian and Russian Foreign Ministers were meeting to discuss a mutual military aid treaty.

He recalled that Mrs Smith had said that they did not need much time to complete their work and here were the first signs of a potential crisis. Were the two things connected? he wondered.

A brief notice on Langford's movements also held his attention. Langford was reported to have flown to Aden on what was described as a fact finding mission. At least, Fletcher thought, the British Government appeared to be aware of what was going on. He only hoped they had not sent the wrong man to find out the facts.

A few minutes before four-thirty he told Tonya he was going to make his routine call to the Smiths. For a moment it appeared as if she was going to join him, so he hurriedly pointed out that she should remain in the office in case of any further telephone calls. Her decision hung on a hair's breadth, but finally she agreed. But Fletcher still had to be careful. The telephone kiosk was close to the office and in full view from the office window.

In the kiosk he quickly dialled Buckley's home, but as he expected got no response. He then phoned Buckley's paper.

'Mr Buckley, one moment please, I will put you through to his office,' came the crisp reply to his enquiry.

And a few seconds later.

'Mr Buckley's office.'

'I would like to speak to Mr Buckley.'

'I am afraid he is not in at the moment. This is his secretary speaking.'

Fletcher cursed. The dice were not falling in his favour. He had to be quick.

'Where is he?'

'He is at a press conference at the Ministry of Defence. Who is calling?'

He ignored the question.

'Will you be able to get a message to him?'

'Yes, he usually phones through. Is it important?'

'Yes, it is. Tell him that the appointment he has for this evening has been brought forward one hour.'

'Who shall I say phoned?'

Fletcher hesitated for only a second. If he didn't give a name she might disregard the message.

'Mr Fletcher,' he said and rang off.

His real name was known only to British Intelligence. Even if the Smiths managed to trace the call the name would mean nothing to them. But it would to Buckley.

He quickly dialled the travel agency.

'I wish to know the arrangements for Mrs Adams' flight to Paris on Friday evening,' he said.

After a brief pause the receptionist who answered the phone gave him the details.

'Mrs Adams is booked on the B.E.A. flight number 356, leaving London Airport at nineteen hundred hours.'

'Thank you.'

Fletcher returned to the office. He explained his delay by complaining that the line was engaged, but if Tonya was suspicious she didn't show it. Unfortunately she delayed her return to Redhill until the last moment. If she had gone earlier, he would have phoned Buckley again, but by the time he had taken her to the station it was approaching six-thirty. With mounting impatience he collected his car from the garage.

He had estimated it would take him about forty-five minutes to get to the Bridge Inn, but the evening build-up of traffic held him back and when he did eventually arrive at the Inn it was ten minutes after the new proposed meeting time.

Eagerly he scanned the car park. There were only three cars and one was Buckley's.

'Thank God,' he muttered.

Buckley's car still had its side lights on as if he had just arrived and as Fletcher drew alongside he could see Buckley sitting behind the steering wheel. Fletcher took a quick glance around the park, saw that it was deserted and walked over to join him.

He opened Buckley's passenger door, but as he did so he saw Buckley's body slump forward! The quiet of the night was suddenly shattered as Buckley's head hit the large rimmed horn on the steering column.

Desperately, Fletcher pulled Buckley's body back off the horn and restored its delicate equilibrium. The car stank of gunpowder and as Fletcher took away his hand he noticed it was covered with blood.

There was a gentle thud to the right of Buckley's body as a revolver fell out of his hand and landed on the floor.

Fletcher groaned. He had been too late! Buckley was dead! The right side of his head had been blown out by a gun fired at close range.

Cautiously, he glanced around to see if the noise of the horn had attracted anyone. Fortunately it was still early for diners and no one was to be seen. He closed the car door and wiped his finger prints off the handle.

As he returned to his own car his brain was furiously determining what to do. If he went into the hotel and reported the incident, he would become involved. If he didn't, he ran the risk of having been seen. It was the lesser of the two evils. He had to get way from the vicinity at once.

Still watching for any sign of life, he swiftly drove away from the hotel. But he couldn't go far, the mileage on the indicator on the dashboard had to be realistic when he got back to Redhill. He pulled into a narrow track leading to a copse about two miles from the hotel and lit a cigarette.

He felt sick and guilty. He had been responsible for getting Buckley to the Inn. He had been responsible for his death. But eight-thirty had been the proposed time, not seven-thirty. How had they got to know about the change?

Buckley must have got his message otherwise he could not have arrived so early. He must have travelled direct from Whitehall.

There were only two possibilities. Either Buckley had been followed from Whitehall; in which case no matter what Fletcher had done he would still have been murdered, or somehow they had got hold of his message.

Fletcher cursed himself for the way he had bungled the whole business. He had been unprepared for such a situation, but there was no excuse. He should have had an agreed distress signal with British Security.

He also cursed Buckley for bringing the Smiths out into the open. It had been suicidal. No matter what Fletcher had done they would have eventually silenced Buckley. Their organisation was so powerful and so desperate.

Fletcher realised he had placed himself in a nasty position. They would wonder why Buckley had arrived so early and they would try to find out. Only if Buckley had been followed was Fletcher safe. The murderer would have left the Bridge Inn immediately he had fired the shot. He would not have been there when Fletcher arrived and Fletcher had not passed any cars coming from the Inn on the last few miles of his journey.

If Fletcher turned up at the appointed time, he could still bluff it out. That was if Buckley had been followed. But if they knew of his message? He would have to deny it. He would swear he knew nothing about it.

There was one glimmer of hope. They had achieved their object. Buckley was dead. Perhaps they would let the matter rest at that.

At twenty minutes past eight he returned along the road to the hotel. As he drove the car slowly back to the scene of the crime, he wondered who had done the killing. Smith, Mikolyn or Timovitch?

Smith and Mikolyn knew Buckley well enough to get close to him without arousing too much suspicion. They could have even have exchanged greetings. And what about Timovitch? He had a motorcycle. He could have easily followed Buckley from Whitehall.

It could also have been a hired gunman. Even in London there were men who would kill for money. But the Communists very rarely brought in outsiders. It was too risky. No, it was either one of their cell or someone else within the organisation.

As he approached the inn, he saw the blue flashing lights of an ambulance in the car park. He drove straight past and returned to Redhill.

Chapter Fourteen

The following morning the papers were mainly concerned with the mounting trouble in the Middle East and there was no reference to Buckley's death. The evening papers, however, printed the story in full and although suicide was not mentioned the inference was there.

Tonya was unusually quiet the whole day and made no attempt to discuss the subject, nor did she read the evening newspapers.

Fletcher waited anxiously for any developments. But the next few days brought no apparent reaction from the Smiths or the police.

Tonya did not let any feelings she may have been suppressing interfere with her work. She phoned Lady Manning and professed to be both shocked and aghast at the news. The Mannings were similarly stunned. So also was Ian Grey who surprisingly phoned Fletcher to talk over the affair.

Fletcher began to realise the extent Buckley had gone to in his inquiries when he learned that Grey had also recently been in Buckley's company. They had met at an Insurance function and, like Fletcher and Tonya, Buckley had developed his friendship. How little he knew about the real truth, Fletcher thought. He and his wife were an innocent couple who had come under Buckley's cloud of suspicion, simply because their holiday in Spain had coincided with that of the Mannings.

Ian Grey wished to attend Buckley's funeral and they agreed to go together. But they had to wait until the findings of the inquest which was scheduled to take place later that week. Fletcher awaited the verdict with interest. For the sake of both

Buckley's aged father, who was his closest living relative and the record, he hoped that a verdict of suicide would not be established.

As it turned out an open verdict was recorded. Two interesting facts had been sufficient to rule out suicide. It was established that Buckley was left-handed and yet the revolver which had caused his death was found by the right hand side of his body.

The second finding surprised Fletcher. The time of death was estimated at seven p.m. and the body had not been discovered until seven-forty-five. Shortly before seven-thirty one of the two customers at the inn had arrived and in his evidence he stated that Buckley's car was not in the car park.

If the time of death was correct, it implied that Buckley had been killed elsewhere and his body taken to the Bridge Inn. It was obvious that the Smith's carefully made plans had come unstuck and other plans of execution hurriedly carried out.

The funeral took place in a small village in Buckinghamshire. It was a depressing ceremony made even more dismal by the torrential rain which persisted all day.

Ian Grey accompanied Fletcher and Tonya, but his wife remained at home. Inside the church all the pews were occupied and they had to join a group standing at the rear. Many notable people were at the service and most of the people Fletcher had met at the Manning's cocktail party were also present, including the Mannings themselves, Langford, Davies and Prentice. The Smiths, however, were conspicuous by their absence.

After the service, Fletcher had a brief word with Sir Joseph and his family. Susan Manning looked pale and drawn and was obviously deeply upset. She stood close to her father, unconcerned about the soaking they were getting and uninterested in Fletcher's company.

She worried him. Her present feelings were understandable, but her attitude since her return from their holidays had noticeably changed. Something had happened to bring about this change and he felt Mikolyn was somehow connected.

She was still on his mind when he reached his car. As Tonya and Ian Grey waited patiently on the narrow pavement for him to unlock the car, he fumbled in his rain soaked pocket for the key. When he brought it out, however, a small printed card fell to the ground. He was hidden from Tonya and Ian Grey by the car and as he unlocked and opened the doors, he deftly retrieved the card and unnoticed put it back in his pocket.

The card had not been in his pocket when he had arrived. It had been slipped in when they had been standing in the church or gathered around the grave. It could have been put there by one of a hundred.

He made certain it didn't fall out again. Nor did he attempt to examine it until he was on his own.

The card bore the name and address of a garage in Hendon, the Avon Motor Company and advertised a twenty-four-hour repair and taxi service. But on the reverse side was written a name — his name. Fletcher. It was a name known only to British Intelligence. Alongside it was a brief message — 'if you need assistance.'

At last they had considered it advisable to make contact with him. Buckley's death had hotted up the pace. If only they had made their move sooner.

He memorised the address and telephone number and destroyed the card. He didn't feel quite so isolated now, he knew he had friends. It bolstered his morale and gave him renewed confidence.

If the Smiths made no direct move to indicate they suspected him of interfering with Buckley's execution, the subsequent change in their routine and in Tonya's attitude, gave cause for anxiety.

At the following meeting with Timovitch everything appeared normal until Timovitch told him that all future meetings were cancelled. They were now in their sixth month, the month which was supposed to have been critical. It was a time when he would have expected the greatest activity and the most frequent meetings.

Their work, however, was to continue and their reports were to be sent by post to a box number at the G.P.O. in Croydon, where, no doubt, a friend in the Post Office service would channel them to the Smiths.

Tonya's attitude was a mystery. At times she appeared edgy and irritable as if she had something on her mind, whilst at other times she was her customary cold, confident, unapproachable self. But she never left his side. Any suggestion that she should meet Lady Manning on her own also met with disapproval. It was as if she was giving him no opportunity to be on his own for any length of time.

Fortunately, the police inquiries did not reach him and he assumed that British Security had vetoed any move in his direction. It was ironical, however, that at a time when he felt his own position within the group was in jeopardy, that not only did the international situation take a turn for the worse, but he should also have the most success with the Mannings, on their behalf.

In the Middle East the fuse had been lit. Iran was in a state of revolt and in Iraq the Communist inspired riots were becoming more militant. The Russians were threatening to counter any British move to send in troops and with their recent pact of mutual military aid with the United Arab Republics they appeared to have the upper hand.

With the Mannings, there was considerable activity including a dinner party at the Mannings' home. Also at the dinner were Prentice and his wife and the veteran politician Hugh Davies.

Davies was in fine form and kept the party entertained and even Prentice was more agreeable than he had been on the previous occasion they had met. But despite his more relaxed manner, Prentice still managed to remain aloof. By the end of the evening Fletcher was no closer to the man than he was at the beginning and he was thankful that it was Sir Joseph and not Prentice, who was their target.

Both Sir Joseph and Davies were extremely friendly and with Sir Joseph, Fletcher knew their friendship was now on a firm footing.

The culmination of their social encounters with the Mannings was a charity ball held in the Savoy Hotel. Lady Manning was one of the patrons of the charity and invited Fletcher and Tonya to join a small private party for the function. Langford, Prentice and Davies were also in the party.

Susan Manning on this occasion looked particularly attractive. Her long sleek blonde hair glistened and her eyes sparkled. It was the first time Fletcher had seen her since Buckley's funeral and the contrast in mood and surroundings between the two events was reflected both in her face and appearance.

If Fletcher had been honest with himself he would have admitted that he was attracted to her, but he had long since learned that in his business personal feelings had to be closely guarded or they could prove fatal.

He did dance with her, however, but for a different reason. He wanted to see her reactions when he mentioned Vincent's name.

'We haven't seen very much of you recently,' he remarked as they danced around the floor.

'I have been rather busy,' she replied.

She didn't look at him as she spoke.

'How is Vincent?' he asked casually.

'Oh, don't you know?' she asked with surprise.

'No, I'm afraid we have been rather neglecting him recently.'

'I haven't seen him for a while, either.'

She purposely changed the subject, but Fletcher later tried again.

'Why don't we fix an evening for you to come and have dinner and we'll invite Vincent also. In that way we can make up for our shortcomings and also have the pleasure of your company.'

'That would be very nice,' she said politely, 'but if you don't mind would you leave it for a while. I really am tied up for the next few weeks.'

Her refusal was pointed and her excuse lame. As if realising her lack of grace she added more tenderly: 'Don't think me rude, Paul, but I would rather leave it for a while.'

'Certainly. I can understand your having a full social diary.'

'It's not that,' she said quickly, 'but…'

She went no further. Whatever she intended to say remained unsaid.

It was obvious something was bothering her. Something had happened to turn her against Mikolyn. He cursed the man for his stupidity and only hoped that if she had confided in anyone it was not someone who could foul up their play before the final scene was acted.

At the end of their dance she left him and returned to her own private party. He was still no further forward.

The ball was a memorable occasion because as events turned out it was the last time they met the Mannings socially, but Fletcher was also given further cause to remember the evening when they returned to their house in Redhill.

They were in their bedroom — the room where they slept. Even here they had to keep up the pretence and it was only a pretence. Tonya was combing her hair and Fletcher was getting undressed. Suddenly without warning, she turned to face him.

'Buckley did have to be killed?' she asked.

The question shook Fletcher both in its subject matter and in the rather gentle tone she had used.

Automatically, he became suspicious. Tonya could play many parts very convincingly, but behind them all was her cool, granite belief in the Soviet cause.

What was she up to?

'He was a British agent,' Fletcher snapped.

'I know,' Tonya said evenly, 'but did we have to kill him?'

'My God!' Fletcher exclaimed, genuinely surprised that she should voice any doubts. 'This is not a game. It is a deadly business. It was him or us.'

'I suppose so.'

She continued to brush her hair.

'We are right, Dimitri, aren't we?'

She had used his assumed Russian name for the first time. She was openly flaunting the first basic principles of their security.

She didn't wait for an answer.

'I mean, in what we are doing.'

Fletcher tried to make his reply sound as incredulous as possible.

'Do you know what you are saying?' he asked aghast.

'Yes, Dimitri, I know what I am saying,' she snapped, but added more evenly, 'but I want you to tell me what we are doing is necessary.' There was a plea in her voice.

She looked at him appealingly.

Fletcher lit a cigarette to give him time to think. Was she genuinely doubting her work? Or was she testing him? Her attitude recently had been very strange, ever since Buckley's death. It could have affected her. On the other hand it could be a try out.

There had been no reaction from the Smiths, but that didn't mean they had forgotten. Timovitch had stopped their meetings, that had been ominous. And if she was only pretending, what was she expecting him to do? To admit his real identity and win her over to his cause? It had been done before.

A not very convincing reply to her question would be the start, followed up by further evening discussions, each time agreeing with her that there was doubts and finally admitting his role. But that wouldn't help him. Nor would it help her if she was really genuine. He was so close to the final act that nothing, absolutely nothing, had to stand in his way — not even Tonya.

'Are you actually doubting our cause?' he asked in a hushed tone, as if the mere utterance of the words would bring the wrath of the Kremlin into the bedroom.

'I don't know, Dimitri,' she said quietly, 'I don't know.'

Fletcher stood up and slowly paced the room, desperately trying to recall all the communist dogmas, platitudes and arguments. She was waiting eagerly for him to say something and he knew that what he said and how she reacted could seriously affect his future.

If it was a try out he had to convince her of his authenticity, or his life would be in danger. If she was genuine, then he had to dissuade her for fear Timovitch or the Smiths got wind of it and altered their plans.

He fell back on one of the Communist's favourite lines when they wanted to stir up anti-west feeling — the fear of a German military revival.

Slowly, but with mounting feeling he reminded her about the war and how their country had been ransacked at the hands of the Germans. He accused the Germans of still being warmongers and the British and Americans of being dupes, building up the German war machine so that they could get their revenge. He pointed out that it was only the nuclear strength of the Soviet army which prevented another war and how essential their work was in preventing the West from taking the lead.

From the international front he turned his attack to domestic matters. He exalted the communist system and scorned the capitalist way of life and claimed that she belonged to the Communists and owed everything to them.

His arguments were almost word perfect to the propaganda lectures that he had occasionally been subjected to at the Smiths. He could see that her brainwashed mind was responding to his reasoning like a drug addict receiving a booster.

When he had finished, Tonya, who had remained quiet throughout his long speeches, gave him a long, gentle look.

'Dimitri,' she said softly, 'you have changed in so many ways. You were so selfish and inconsiderate, but I have watched you here in England and you are different. You are gentle and understanding. I never knew anyone could change so much.

Those years in Moscow must have made an impression on you.'

Fletcher listened to her confession with both guilt and apprehension. His deceit would soon be exposed. He had never thought what would happen to Tonya when the moment came for him to contact the British Security. He wanted her to stop praising him, he didn't want her to like him. It would only aggravate the position. When she was resentful of him he at least knew where he stood, but now she was talking to him with tenderness.

He watched her take off her house coat. She was wearing an unusually flimsy negligee which exposed all the curves of her firm, sensual body.

She got into bed.

'Come and sleep with me tonight, Dimitri,' she said in a whisper, but there was both eagerness and promise in her rather breathless tone.

Fletcher took off his dressing gown and put out the light.

Chapter Fifteen

During the following days, Fletcher became acutely aware of how little he knew about what was going on and how vulnerable he was to any form of retribution the Smiths might hand out. He had a feeling of foreboding. The Smiths suspected him, he felt certain. Tonya had shown that. Just how much they knew was the question.

Tonya's lapse was never repeated. Her love making had been passionate, eager, desperate, as if time was running out, but it had been another try out, a clumsy attempt to make Fletcher expose himself.

He had succumbed to her physical overtures, but her cajoling, innuendoes and veiled promises had fallen on stony ground. It had been a lapse into the realms of fantasy. Her attempt had failed and the subject was never discussed again, or any other advances made. It brought them no closer to each other and lifted no barriers. She was again Tonya Sklevosky, cold and efficient. Again the enigma, as were her faceless masters in the Kremlin.

They followed their normal daily routine, but Fletcher watched every move. Something was going to happen soon, everything pointed to it.

On the international scene the clouds were black and ugly. Iran was now in a state of open rebellion and although the Government forces had remained loyal the peacock throne was not very secure.

In Iraq a similar progression from communist riots to open rebellion was taking place.

Britain's lifeline was in danger. Troops had been rushed to Aden and in true Palmerston style the fleet was anchored off the canal. The intervention of British troops in Iran itself was being considered and an existing treaty between the two countries allowed for such a move, if the Government of Iran asked for help. But it was the threat of the Russians to send in their own troops if Britain intervened that held up such a move.

The situation was delicate and the cold reception being received in the States to British overtures for support did not help. The Americans were not so concerned about the Middle East as the British. They had no need to be. They had their own supplies of oil. And the situation was not unlike their own recent trouble in Panama and the criticism given to them by the British Government and press still rankled.

On the fourth of November the Prime Minister flew to Washington for talks with the President. In his party was the Minister of Defence. The reports from the talks were favourable. On the surface at least, their differences appeared to have been patched up and an agreed course of action determined. Two days later the Prime Minister returned to London to report to his cabinet.

It was a cold, damp, foggy day. In his office Fletcher listened to the lunch time news on the radio. The Prime Minister's plane had been diverted from London Airport to a R.A.F. Station in Oxford. He was due to arrive in the city during the afternoon.

Fletcher felt restless and uneasy. Tonya had suddenly come out with the news the previous evening that she had arranged to spend the day with Lady Manning and her son, who was home from school. When he tackled her on how and when she had made the arrangements, she claimed it was a long standing agreement she had made with Lady Manning. They were spending the afternoon in the city and in the evening were taking Lady Manning's son to a circus in Guildford. A few weeks back he would have accepted such an explanation without question, but now it was his turn to be suspicious.

Since Buckley's death Tonya had never left him on his own for any length of time. Why should she suddenly do it now?

During the afternoon he was given further grounds for speculation. At four p.m. precisely the phone rang. It was Mikolyn. In a disguised conversation he told Fletcher that Timovitch wanted to see him in the office that evening. Fletcher's hopes soared. There had been no contact with Timovitch for weeks now and there was no track meeting at the stadium that particular evening. Something was in the wind.

It was after seven when Timovitch arrived. Mikolyn was with him. Timovitch looked tense. Mikolyn was stiff, formal and on edge. Fletcher noticed he was carrying a grip bag.

There was no formal greeting.

'You are late,' Fletcher said, 'I was getting worried.'

Timovitch glanced at Mikolyn and scowled, but ignored Fletcher's remark.

'We must act quickly,' he said. 'How long will it take you to get to Richmond Park?'

'In this fog about forty-five minutes,' Fletcher said. 'Why?'

'Too long,' Timovitch snapped. 'You must do it in thirty. Let's go.'

There was no discussion, no explanation, only action. Fletcher didn't like it at all.

Richmond Park at this time of the year was a quiet, desolate area, even without the swirling fog. In the car he felt a cold chill run down his spine. Timovitch and Mikolyn were both slumped in the corners of the rear seat and the only conversation which took place was the occasional remark from Timovitch telling him which route to take. Was this going to be a one way trip for him? Were they going to deal with him as they had with Buckley?

He fumbled in his pockets for his cigarettes and felt a little easier when he had assured himself that his small automatic pistol was still in his pocket.

The journey took longer than the thirty minutes Timovitch had granted him and as each patch of fog slowed their progress Fletcher could sense Timovitch becoming more and more impatient. When they did reach the park Timovitch sat forward in his seat and Fletcher could hear the man's heavy breathing close to his face.

They entered the park through the Robin Hood Gate and drove slowly along the narrow roadway. In the car the atmosphere was tense. They approached a crossroad and the twin sidelights of a vehicle loomed up out of the fog.

Timovitch gave a grunt and ordered Fletcher to pull alongside the vehicle. In an instant the atmosphere changed, but although Timovitch was now relaxed, Fletcher was still on edge. The strain of driving through the fog had not made matters any easier for him.

The vehicle making the rendezvous with them was a black, London-type taxi and as he stopped alongside it Fletcher made a mental note of its registration number and of the features of the bored looking driver. But he was unable to distinguish who the passenger was in the cab, all he could see was the red glow of a cigarette.

Timovitch told Fletcher and Mikolyn to remain in the car whilst he got out and entered the taxi. Fletcher lit a cigarette and offered one to Mikolyn. Mikolyn refused and as Fletcher replaced his cigarettes back in his pocket he eased his automatic out on to his lap.

'What's happening?' Fletcher said.

But Mikolyn wasn't going to be drawn. He just shrugged and remained mute.

A few minutes later Timovitch returned. Fletcher watched him retake his seat. He heard the taxi move off and waited for Timovitch to make his move.

'Get changed,' Timovitch said to Mikolyn.

Mikolyn seemed to have been expecting the instruction and quickly opened his grip bag and set about changing his clothes. His actions both surprised and relieved Fletcher. Whatever they were planning was not directed at him. Timovitch's following remark made his relief complete.

'If all goes well tonight, Comrade,' he said to Fletcher, 'your work will be finished. You will be flying home.'

There was a sting in the tail which Fletcher didn't miss, but he would cross that bridge when he came to it. For the present, at least, he was safe.

'What do we have to do?' he asked.

In the dim light he saw Timovitch give a wry smile.

'Get a copy of Operation Pipeline, that's all.'

'Operation Pipeline?' Fletcher asked.

'Yes, Comrade. It is the code name for a military operation in the Middle East. An operation which the British intend to implement within the next twenty-four hours.'

Fletcher listened stunned. He hadn't anticipated the British Government would call the Russians' bluff.

'What about the Americans?' he asked.

'It has their blessing,' Timovitch said.

So that was why the P.M. flew to Washington, Fletcher thought.

'We must get a copy of that operation,' Timovitch said. He sounded determined.

Fletcher asked: 'How?'

'One hour ago,' Timovitch said, 'a copy of the operation was handed to Sir Joseph Manning. He is now studying it at his home in Guildford. Tomorrow he will give his comments on it to the Minister, before it goes to the full cabinet for their approval.'

My God, Fletcher thought, how the hell does he know all this?

'So you see, Comrade,' Timovitch added, 'it will not be so difficult after all.'

There was something in his tone which made Fletcher suspicious. Were they expecting him to get hold of the operation? He glanced at Mikolyn. He was zipping up a black leather jacket. On his feet were a pair of black plimsoles. His trousers were also black.

'What is the plan?' Fletcher said.

'We leave immediately for Sir Joseph's home in Guildford,' Timovitch explained. 'There are two policemen patrolling the house, but that shouldn't unduly concern us. When we get to Guildford you will drop Vincent and me at a location close to Sir Joseph's house. You will then go and visit Sir Joseph.'

'On what pretext?' Fletcher asked.

'That is up to you, Comrade. I am sure you can think up a plausible excuse.'

Fletcher ignored the sarcasm.

'You won't have to stay long,' Timovitch continued. 'Only long enough for Vincent to take a photograph of the operation.'

Fletcher was beginning to understand. Mikolyn was going to break in.

'Sir Joseph always does his work in his study,' Timovitch explained, 'but he never entertains in that room. You have to get him out of the study long enough for Vincent to get in and out. Understand?'

Fletcher nodded his head. He understood only too well. It was a straightforward burglary.

'How does Vincent get in?' he asked.

Timovitch smiled. 'We have not been idle,' he said. 'We have a duplicate of all the necessary keys, even the safe.'

Fletcher listened astounded.

'What about Lady Manning?' he asked.

'She is at a circus in Guildford with her son … and your wife.'

So Tonya's arrangements with Lady Manning were part of their scheme, he thought. It had not been a long standing agreement after all. It also meant that she had been in contact with Timovitch or Mikolyn without him knowing. He wondered what else had gone on behind his back.

'And Susan Manning?' he asked.

He could see Timovitch scowl.

'She is taken care of.'

'What do you mean?'

'Let us say we have her under custody so that she cannot interfere.'

Fletcher was aghast. What had happened to her.

Mikolyn spoke for the first time.

'Don't worry,' he said, 'she will not be harmed.'

He gave an infuriating laugh.

'My God,' Fletcher exclaimed. 'You blundered! You idiot!'

Timovitch quickly intervened.

'She has been suspicious for a while,' he snapped. 'She wouldn't co-operate, so we had no alternative. We cannot afford to let this opportunity pass us by.'

'Where is she?' Fletcher demanded.

'Don't worry yourself, Comrade. She is being well taken care of.'

Fletcher felt dejected. If anything happened to her he would never forgive himself, but he couldn't pursue the matter without appearing obvious.

'So the family is out of the way,' he said. 'Who is left?'

'Only the housekeeper.'

'Is she one of us?'

Timovitch smiled.

'She is harmless.'

'But is she one of us?' Fletcher persisted.

'You ask too many questions,' Timovitch said sharply. 'Too much knowledge can be dangerous.'

Fletcher had got his answer.

'What if Sir Joseph will not see me?'

'You underestimate your ability,' Timovitch said lightly, but added with deadly seriousness. 'But if Sir Joseph is not co-operative Vincent will have to take other measures.'

Fletcher didn't require any further explanations. He knew what Timovitch meant.

But Timovitch didn't intend the warning to stop there.

'And if Vincent should fail, we have his family. I am sure he would not like to see anything happen to his daughter, or his son.'

The bastards, Fletcher thought. The bastards!

'What if Sir Joseph brings his papers into the lounge with him?' he asked.

'In that case, Comrade, Vincent will have to wait until he returns to his study.'

They had all the answers, but there was no finesse about their plans. It was bold, simple, unsophisticated, but not in the Soviet pattern. There were too many loose ends.

'Come, it is time to go,' Timovitch snapped.

The journey to Guildford was a slow silent affair. Timovitch and Mikolyn again slunk in the corner seats and the fog still lingered in patches.

Fletcher collected his thoughts together. What they proposed to do didn't ring true. Why should Sir Joseph have a copy of the operation at his home? He was not even a member of the cabinet. He may have been consulted, kept informed, or even asked to comment, but the British Government were surely not so stupid as to allow them to be taken out of Whitehall, or were they? Were they so blind and innocent? No, he couldn't believe that. There was more to it. Something more sinister, more cunning. Who had been the person in the taxi? Had it been Smith? Or was it someone else? Someone who had just left Sir Joseph? If only he had seen the face behind the cigarette.

He thought of Tonya. She was in on it. That meant she had been meeting Timovitch secretly. Why had she not told him? Why? And why were they being shipped back to Moscow? Was it because of Susan Manning? Because she had found out about Mikolyn? Or was there some other reason?

Fletched didn't believe Timovitch's story, but he knew he would have to play along with it until he found the real answer. Not because of the threat to Sir Joseph's family, which he felt was real enough, but because of the enormity of what they hoped to achieve. He now knew their aim. Somehow he had to stop them getting it.

As they approached Guildford, Timovitch again took over and directed Fletcher to a lonely country lane.

'This lane leads to the rear of Sir Joseph's house,' Timovitch explained. 'It is now eight-forty. By eight-forty-five you will have arrived at Sir Joseph's house. You should be in the lounge talking to Sir Joseph by eight-fifty. That will give Vincent time to get to the house. You must keep Sir Joseph occupied for at least fifteen minutes, longer if possible. When you leave Sir Joseph come straight back here.'

'How will you know when I am in the lounge?'

'Don't worry yourself, Comrade,' Timovitch said. 'We will know when you and Sir Joseph are in the lounge — and when you arrive and leave the house.' He said no more and Fletcher let the matter drop. They had something up their sleeve. Something which they didn't intend to tell him about. He decided to heed the warning. If they suspected him and everything pointed that way, they would certainly make sure he didn't make a false move.

Mikolyn fitted a silencer on to his revolver and placed it in his pocket. Timovitch slipped out of the car and Mikolyn followed him. Fletcher waited a couple of minutes and then drove the short distance to Sir Joseph's house. At precisely eight-forty-five he pulled up outside the entrance porch and got out.

'Evening, Sir.'

The burly figure of a uniformed policeman loomed up from the side of the entrance porch.

'Good evening, Constable,' Fletcher said.

The constable eyed him closely.

'Have you an appointment with Sir Joseph?' he asked.

'No, I haven't, but I am a personal friend of Sir Joseph's. What the devil is all this about?'

'Just taking precautions, Sir, that's all.'

The constable rang the doorbell.

'Nasty night, Sir,' he said.

Fletcher agreed.

The housekeeper opened the door, but before she or Fletcher had time to speak the constable intervened.

'Do you know this man?' he asked.

The housekeeper looked at Fletcher.

'Why yes, Constable,' she said. 'It is Mr Adams. He is a friend of Sir Joseph's.'

'That's all right, then, Sir. Sorry to have bothered you.'

The policeman stood aside and Fletcher entered the hallway.

'I would like to see Sir Joseph,' he said when the entrance door had been closed.

'Oh dear, Mr Adams. Sir Joseph is very busy. He said he was not to be disturbed on any account.'

'This is terribly important,' Fletcher persisted. 'I must see Sir Joseph. Please tell him I am here.'

'Well, Mr Adams, he was very emphatic.'

'Please,' Fletcher insisted. 'It is a matter of utmost importance.'

For a moment he thought he was going to be turned away.

'Come into the lounge, then and I will let Sir Joseph know you are here.'

Fletcher sighed. If she was working for the Reds she had acted her part very convincingly.

He followed her into the lounge and watched her switch on the various table lamps. She was a woman in her late fifties, matronly and homely in appearance. Was Timovitch bluffing? he wondered. Was she innocent? But he recalled she had not been in the employ of the Mannings for very long and gave Timovitch the benefit of the doubt.

He decided to try a long shot.

'Has Mr Langford been here this evening?' he asked. 'I understand he intended to call on Sir Joseph.' He was thinking of the person in the taxi.

'Mr Langford?' She asked in surprise. 'Oh no, Sir, he hasn't been here … only Mr Davies.'

Davies! He looked at her sharply, but she had her back to him and was leaving the room. Davies. Why had she volunteered the information? Had it been accidental or intentional? How much credence could be put on her remark? Had Davies really visited Sir Joseph? It opened up an interesting field of conjecture.

He glanced anxiously at his watch. It was nine o'clock. If Sir Joseph didn't come out of his study soon Mikolyn would become impatient and desperate.

He started to pace the floor. He had already decided on the line he would take with Sir Joseph, but he had not counted on Sir Joseph refusing to see him. Now he was not so sure.

He heaved a sigh of relief when he saw Sir Joseph appear. Sir Joseph looked much older and more serious than Fletcher had seen him before. It was as if the affairs of state were weighing heavily on his shoulders. As he entered the room he removed the spectacles he was wearing and frowned. He was not pleased to see Fletcher.

'I am very sorry to disturb you, Sir Joseph,' Fletcher said, 'but…'

'I am very busy, Paul,' Sir Joseph interrupted. 'I would appreciate it if you would be as quick as possible. I am expecting an important phone call any minute.' His tone was sharp and unfriendly.

Fletcher was not being put off. He had to keep Sir Joseph out of his study for at least fifteen minutes. He ran his hand nervously through his hair.

'I have got myself into a spot of difficulties with business,' he said quickly, trying to sound as anxious as possible. 'You are one of the few persons whose advice I would respect, otherwise I would not have bothered you.'

Sir Joseph frowned.

'I am very sorry to hear that,' he said. 'Any other time we could have talked it over, but it is impossible tonight. I just cannot spare you the time.' He was emphatic.

Fletcher sighed and looked dejected.

'I will be busy all day tomorrow,' Sir Joseph continued, 'but I think I am free the day after. If you wish we can meet and talk it over then.' His tone had softened, but there was no changing his mind.

'That is very good of you,' Fletcher said.

Sir Joseph had remained standing close to the door. He was waiting for Fletcher to take his leave. Desperately, Fletcher thought of a way to prolong the interview.

'I won't bother you any further,' he said and then as a casual afterthought added: 'Would you mind if I had a whisky before I left? It has been such a hell of a day.'

Sir Joseph mumbled an apology for his inhospitality and walked over to a cocktail cabinet and poured out a whisky and soda. He handed the glass to Fletcher, but didn't have one himself.

Fletcher had watched him thoughtfully as he had prepared the drink. Should he take him into his confidence? he wondered. Should he tell him that at that very moment a Soviet agent was breaking into his study and photographing his documents? That his daughter was being held captive somewhere and his wife was being escorted by another Soviet Agent. Would it help? Would Sir Joseph believe him? Or would he have to be convinced? But there was one further question even more pertinent — could he trust Sir Joseph? Despite his attitude, he had still left his study and was in the lounge, just as Timovitch had forecast. That settled the issue.

Fletcher accepted the whiskey and drank it slowly, letting the minutes slip by. Sir Joseph stood beside him, awkward and uncommunicative.

'I really am sorry for bursting in on you,' Fletcher said.

'I hope things will not appear so black next time we meet,' Sir Joseph replied in a more friendly tone.

Fletcher finished his drink and glanced at his watch. He had just made the time limit.

They moved to the door.

'I hope your wife soon gets better,' Sir Joseph remarked.

He was not looking at Fletcher as he spoke so he did not see Fletcher's sudden alert expression.

What did he mean, soon get better? Fletcher wondered. Tonya was supposed to be with Lady Manning at a circus.

'Oh, it is nothing serious,' he hedged.

'Pity she had to miss the show. I believe it has a very good cast.'

'Yes, it has,' Fletcher agreed. 'Did Lady Manning go by herself?'

'With Peter. He is doing it at school.'

School? Cast? It sounded more like a Shakespearean play than a circus.

'It is thick in town,' Fletcher said probing. 'I hope she didn't take the car.'

'No, she will get a taxi back.'

So they are in town, Fletcher thought, not in Guildford as Timovitch had said. Timovitch had been lying. He had wanted Fletcher to believe they were out of town, out of the way. Somewhere where they could be taken care of if necessary. Why? What was his game?

They were in the hallway now.

'I will just check with my diary,' Sir Joseph said, 'and make sure I am free on Thursday. It is in the study.'

He left Fletcher and opened the study door before Fletcher could think up an excuse to stop him. Fletcher's hand went automatically to his revolver in his side pocket. But there was no commotion or sound as Sir Joseph entered the room. Mikolyn was not there!

Fletcher followed Sir Joseph into the room. Sir Joseph crossed over to a large desk and picked up a red diary. Fletcher glanced around the room. It was both a study and a library. Around the walls were rows of books. In the centre of the room was the desk and in front of a coal fire were two easy chairs. There was no sign of any papers or documents lying around. He looked at the heavy draped curtains over the french doors and wondered if Mikolyn had, in fact, entered the room.

'Yes, Thursday will be all right,' Sir Joseph said. 'Shall we say one o'clock at the Commons?'

'That is very good of you,' Fletcher muttered.

He didn't let the interview drag on any longer and quickly took his leave. He wanted a few minutes to himself before rejoining Timovitch and Mikolyn.

He drove the car down the drive, on to the main road and pulled in alongside the kerb. Thoughtfully he lit a cigarette. As he had left the house, he had seen the two policemen standing alongside the porch. It was obvious Sir Joseph had in his possession something of national importance, otherwise he would not have been given police protection. Fletcher knew a police watch didn't normally extend below Ministerial rank unless there was a special reason.

Everything Timovitch had said had been proved correct, everything that he had forecast had taken place. There were three possible ways he had got his information. The person in the taxi had visited Sir Joseph and so knew what was going on. The housekeeper was working for them and had passed the information on to someone and finally — either Sir Joseph himself, or someone very close to the Minister, was in league with the Communists — and there wouldn't be many who were aware of Operation Pipeline at this stage.

He pulled slowly away from the kerb. Why had they lied to him about Tonya? he wondered and why had she not taken him into her confidence?

As an afterthought he stopped the car again and checked to see if his automatic was loaded. It was just as well he did. The cartridge case was empty! The bullets had been removed!

Chapter Sixteen

They were waiting for him in the lane. Timovitch got in the car and sat behind Fletcher.

'Let Vincent drive,' he ordered.

'Why?' Fletcher asked with surprise.

'He knows where we are going.'

Fletcher hesitated, but thought better about it and moved over into the passenger seat. As Mikolyn got into the car Fletcher glanced across at him. His clothes were damp from the rain and fog, but there was no mud or dirt on his plimsoles. For a man who was supposed to have crossed over Sir Joseph's lawn and gardens they looked remarkably clean.

'You did well, Comrade,' Timovitch said. He gave a low rumbling laugh. 'You sounded very convincing.'

Fletcher swung round in his seat.

'How did you…' He did not finish his question. Timovitch, a mocking smile on his face, was holding up a small metal box for him to see. Fletcher didn't recognise the pattern, but knew its purpose. It was a small, but powerful, transistor type receiver.

The Russians had perfected the use of radio electronics for their spy work. This was one of their gadgets. Fletcher realised in a flash what had happened. The lounge had been bugged. Somewhere in that room they had planted one of their micro type transmitters.

Now he knew what Timovitch had meant when he had said they would know when Sir Joseph was in the lounge. He remembered how the housekeeper had gone around the room switching on the table lamps. At the same time she could have switched on their transmitter. She was working for them after all. That meant he could discount her remark about Davies.

As if reading his thoughts Timovitch asked: 'Why were you so interested in who had been visiting Sir Joseph?'

'Why shouldn't I be?' Fletcher snapped. 'His movements have always been my concern.'

Timovitch didn't reply.

'What about Sir Joseph's papers?' Fletcher asked.

'Child's play,' Mikolyn said scornfully. 'The fool had left them in his briefcase.'

Fletcher froze in his seat. There had been no briefcase in the study. Mikolyn was lying! He had been nowhere near the house. The whole idea had sounded absurd from the very beginning. Now Fletcher knew it was all a pack of lies.

As if realising Fletcher was suspicious, Mikolyn withdrew his revolver.

'You better keep this now,' he said to Timovitch.

'I have my own,' Timovitch growled.

Mikolyn put his gun away.

The atmosphere had suddenly become electric.

'Moscow will be very pleased,' Fletcher remarked with forced casualness to ease the tension.

'Yes, they will be pleased to have you back,' Timovitch said. He started to laugh and Mikolyn joined in. It was not a friendly laugh. They were laughing at him — not with him.

But Fletcher was beginning to put the pieces together. They had not stolen anything from Sir Joseph, there was no need to. They had already been given a copy of the operation from their source within the Ministry. From the man at the top who was prepared to sell his country. The man the Smiths wanted to protect, to keep in his high office for just such a vital and critical moment.

Their reason for cultivating Sir Joseph was becoming clear to him now. For a leak of such a magnitude there had to be a scapegoat and Sir Joseph was going to be the scapegoat. He was to be the victim of a very clever frame up — and Fletcher had done the framing!

Now he knew why he and Tonya were being sent back to Moscow that very night. It wasn't only to deliver a copy of the British plans, but also to put the finishing touches to the picture that Sir Joseph had passed on the secret information to the Russians.

Fletcher sat calmly in the passenger seat, his brain furiously completing the jigsaw.

When the British made their move in the Middle East, they were in for a shock. The Russians would be there waiting for them. Alternatively the Russians would forestall them by publicly denouncing the British plans. In the eyes of the Middle Eastern countries the Russian stock would soar, whilst the British would be made to look a second rate, incompetent, diminishing power.

The Russians would be the professionals, the British the amateurs. It would do irreparable harm to the British image.

And when the people in authority on both sides of the Atlantic started asking questions, as they surely would, then the Russians would let it slip out that Fletcher and Tonya were Communist agents. Photographs would be shown of them in Russia, Spain and England and also photographs of them in the company of the Mannings. With a little bit of help the British press would soon have a full story of their work and of their friendship with the Mannings.

Suspicion would be diverted from the real traitor. Fletcher's visit to Sir Joseph would soon come to light. It would be remembered by the housekeeper and the police. It may only have been a brief visit, but it would be recalled that it had coincided with the time when Sir Joseph had actually been studying the British move.

The inference would be obvious and the Russians would encourage it. They would be very subtle and clever. No one would ever realise they were actually instigating the disclosure of Fletcher's work. With one hand they would deny it and with the other add fuel to the fire.

No matter how vehement Sir Joseph professed his innocence, the facts would be against him. At the worst he would be branded as a traitor, at the best a dupe, a simpleton not to be trusted. His political career would be ruined.

But the ramifications would not stop there. The Minister would have to resign, the Government could even fall and the delicate ties with the United States would be shattered. Confidence in British Security would be ruined.

The whole plot became clear to Fletcher now.

Tonya was not with Lady Manning, there was no need for her to be. Nor was Susan Manning a captive. The last thing the Russians would want was to give the impression that Sir Joseph had passed on the information under a threat to his family. There had to be no evidence of any pressure or coercion.

They had made Fletcher believe there was a danger for an entirely different reason. Because they knew who he really was. They knew he was not Dimitri Nickovitch. They knew he was a double agent working for the British, but they had found out too late. There hadn't been time to bring anyone else in. They had kept him under constant surveillance and when they saw he had no contact with British Security they had let him act the final scene.

The threats to Sir Joseph's family and the transmitter planted in the lounge, were all to make sure he played his part and did nothing to upset their plans. So long as he did their work for them they had nothing to lose. Once they got him back to Russia it would be impossible for the British Government to claim he was one of their agents. The world would laugh at them. It would make them look even more stupid and incompetent and by that time the Russians would have worked on him until he had even forgotten his own real identity. He had played right into their hands.

As he watched the wipers battle with the drizzle he felt, for the second time that night, the cold chill of fear. This time the threat was real. Timovitch's revolver was pointing directly at his back. Timovitch had ordered Mikolyn to drive to make sure Fletcher didn't try anything that would stop him being taken to his appointed place of departure. He was being given no opportunity to drive the car off its scheduled route.

Fletcher cursed himself for trying to be so clever. British Security had given him means of contact and he hadn't used it. He had tried to sew the whole thing up before making his move. He had taken them on single-handed. What a fool he had been. If only he had given them some indication of what was happening.

He abruptly stopped criticising himself. It was a waste of energy. He turned his thoughts to a more constructive form of mental gymnastics. There was still time to stop them. All he had to do was escape from the car. Without him their case against Sir Joseph would be groundless and if he contacted British Security in time they could stop any plane leaving the country. He had to get out of their clutches.

He decided to play for time.

'How are we getting out of the country?' he asked.

'Plane,' Timovitch muttered.

Fletcher looked out of the window.

'In this fog?'

'You aren't flying from London Airport,' Timovitch said and laughed. Again Mikolyn joined in and this time Fletcher played along with them.

'Where are we going now?' he asked.

'You ask too many questions, Comrade,' Timovitch said sullenly and again lapsed into silence.

Fletcher glanced casually at the car door handle. It was not in the locked position and was close to his left hand. One quick jerk and the door would open. But he would have to wait until the car stopped and it had to be in the right place. Otherwise a bullet would find its home in his back.

He turned his attentions to Mikolyn. He wasn't used to the car and was driving it carefully, making sure he did nothing which would infringe the law. The fog still lingered in patches and each time it enveloped the car Mikolyn reduced his speed to a crawl. Fletcher didn't think he would have much bother from him — only Timovitch — but the element of surprise was on his side.

He pretended to be unconcerned about the whole business and slouched in his seat. On the rare occasions Mikolyn spoke it was in connection with the route or to curse the fog. Fletcher invariably added some suitable comment, but Timovitch remained silent.

As they approached the city centre Fletcher's nerves began to tingle. It was going to be now or never.

They crossed the river by the Westminster Bridge and drove past the Houses of Parliament and along Whitehall. If they were making for Wembley and the Smiths they had made a wide detour. There was little traffic about and the bright city lights were shrouded in a veil of fog.

At the end of Charing Cross Road, Mikolyn turned into Oxford Street and headed for Hyde Park.

So far all the traffic lights had been in Mikolyn's favour, but as they approached the junction with Park Lane Fletcher saw them change to red. He braced himself. It was the moment he had been waiting for. Despite his droopy, lounging position, every muscle in his body and every reflex, was tensed for the move.

Mikolyn drove into the centre of the road and came to a halt at the lights. In a flash Fletcher had the door open and was out evading a car coming on his inside. He had moved with the speed of a pouncing tiger. The door had opened without a hitch and the suddenness had taken them by surprise. There had been a startled gasp from Mikolyn and Fletcher had felt a hand grab at his body, but there had been no revolver shot. He had been that quick.

Fletcher ran for his life. He knew Timovitch would be following him.

In a matter of seconds he was into Park Lane. He ran past the entrance to the pedestrian subway and turned into one of the side streets. Swiftly he raced down the street, round a corner and past a road junction. When a fog patch engulfed him, he stopped and listened. Footsteps were pounding towards him.

Desperately, he dived into the portico of a nearby building and, with heart pounding, shrunk into the dark shadows of the doorway.

The footsteps came closer. It could only be Timovitch! He heard him pass by and held his breath. Suddenly there was silence again. Timovitch like Fletcher had stopped and was listening. The hunter and the prey had gone to ground.

For what felt like an eternity Fletcher stood motionless in the doorway. A car came slowly along the road, but Fletcher didn't look to see who it was. It moved past the doorway, its headlights dulled by the fog. He heard it stop further along the road and then move off again, but for fear it was a trick he still remained hidden in the shadows.

When another car came along the road and then another, he felt easier. Cautiously and quietly, he retraced his steps until he came to the road junction when again he burst into speed. This time he didn't stop until he came to the welcome lights of Bond Street and even then he only relaxed when he had successfully managed to hail a passing taxi.

'The Avon Garage, Hendon,' he said to the cab driver and sat back and lit a welcome cigarette.

He felt elated now. He was free of them. In a short while he would be able to put the wheels into motion which would prevent them from leaving the country.

It took the taxi twenty minutes to get to the garage and by that time Fletcher had got over his initial feeling of relief and was becoming anxious. Time was not on his side.

The garage attendant eyed him curiously, for a second and then nodded his head both in recognition and to indicate an office inside the building.

Fletcher ran into the garage and saw a light in an office on a balcony. Quickly, he climbed the stairs and entered the room.

'Evening, Mr Fletcher, we have been expecting you.'

Fletcher stopped dead in his tracks. It was not British Security. It was Milne! Milne the innocent looking assistant who helped the Smiths.

'You!' Fletcher gasped. 'My God!'

'Yes, Fletcher. Me.'

There was nothing innocent or gentle about this Milne. His face was hard set, his mouth twisted in a cruel smile and he spoke from behind a revolver which was pointing directly at Fletcher.

Mikolyn followed Fletcher into the room and instantly Fletcher leapt into action again. Before Milne realised what was happening Fletcher had grabbed Mikolyn and pulled him in between himself and the revolver. With everything he could muster he flung Mikolyn across the room towards the small bald headed Milne.

Without further delay he turned to leave the room, only to run straight into the burly figure of Timovitch and a hammer like blow which crashed into his skull. He sank to the floor unconscious.

Chapter Seventeen

Fletcher heard a murmur of voices as he regained consciousness. His head throbbed and as he opened his eyes the light and figures danced about. Gradually he was able to focus his eyes and take stock of his surroundings.

He was sitting on a chair and at his feet was a pool of blood — his blood! He lifted his head to look around the room and the movement sent a shooting pain down the back of his neck. It was the same room as before — Milne's office. Mikolyn and Timovitch were there and also Tonya.

He glanced at Tonya and she gave him a cold, contemptuous scowl. Her veneer was gone. She was displaying her true feelings. Mikolyn had a similar look on his face. Only Timovitch was unconcerned. He sat with his back to Fletcher, sucking a pipe.

He felt someone dab his head gently with a wet cloth and he turned to see who it was.

'Susan,' he whispered hoarsely.

'Hello, Paul,' she said dejectedly, but managed a faint smile.

The mascara on her eyes was smudged as if she had been crying and her coat was torn at the belt. There had been a struggle. She bathed his head gently.

'What is she doing here?' Fletcher demanded hotly.

Milne appeared in front of him.

'Oh, so you are with us again,' he said.

Fletcher repeated his question.

'Why is she here?'

Milne gave a shrug.

'Unfortunately she wouldn't co-operate and started to interfere.'

'I threatened to phone the police,' Susan snapped.

'And we couldn't have that, Fletcher, could we?'

'I still will when I get out of here,' Susan said hotly.

Milne sighed.

'I wish you would tell her, Fletcher, that this is not a game where the players stop when they are tired.'

But Fletcher said nothing. She was upset enough without him telling her just how deadly serious Milne was.

He glanced at the maps and charts on the wall. It was a legitimate garage and taxi service. Like the Smith's travel agency, it was all above reproach. He had not expected to see Milne again, in fact he had forgotten all about him. He had credited the Smiths as being the puppet masters, but now he was not so sure.

'Give him a whisky,' Milne said to Mikolyn.

Mikolyn produced a flask and it was handed to Fletcher. He took a long drink and felt the alcohol flow into his blood. Why are they being so humane? he wondered.

Susan Manning had finished bathing his head and was standing alongside him. He could feel her body close to his, like a frightened rabbit snuggling up for comfort.

Her presence in the room upset his theories. He couldn't see how they would make her fit into their scheme.

From an adjoining room came the muffled sound of a voice over a radio receiver. Milne nodded to Mikolyn who left the room. Fletcher could hear him speaking to the person at the other end of the radio link, but was unable to get the gist of their conversation.

Presently Mikolyn returned.

'Well?' Milne asked.

Mikolyn nodded his head. 'It is clear at Aylesbury,' he said.

Milne beamed with delight. He turned to Tonya and Timovitch. 'You will leave in fifteen minutes,' he said.

The news seemed to please Tonya.

'That is good,' she said.

Fletcher looked at her curiously as she lit a cigarette. She was wearing a leather jacket tied at the waist and leather boots. Gone was her western sophisticated style of clothing. Even her hair style was plain and severe. Had she reverted to her true self? Or had she changed her style to show that she was Tonya Sklevosky again and not Jane Adams?

Milne came over to him.

'You fit to travel?' he asked.

'Would it make any difference?' Fletcher snapped.

Milne smiled. Not the friendly, benign smile Fletcher had seen so often at the training camp, but the confident smile of a man who knew he was going to get his own way.

'Not really, but I don't want you to appear injured.'

'Appear?' Fletcher asked with surprise.

'Oh, yes, Fletcher. You and Miss Manning are going to be seen.'

'Where are you taking us?' Susan demanded.

Milne looked at her and then back at Fletcher.

'Tell her, Fletcher,' he said.

Fletcher sighed. She had to know some time.

'At a guess,' he said, 'I would say Russia.'

'Russia!' she exclaimed. She grabbed his shoulder to steady herself. Fletcher put his hand on hers. 'But that is impossible,' she gasped.

'Miss Manning,' Milne snapped, 'like a lot of people in this country you have your head buried in the sand. It certainly is not impossible. In fifteen minutes precisely you will walk out of here, arm in arm with Fletcher, like two normal people and board a taxi which will be waiting to take you to your place of departure.'

'What makes you so sure?' Fletcher asked.

'I was expecting you to ask that,' Milne said. He looked at Susan Manning again. 'What time is it?' he asked.

She didn't reply she was too stunned.

'It is ten-forty-five,' Milne said, 'and do you know where your stepmother and brother are at this precise moment?'

'No,' Susan whispered.

'Then let me tell you,' Milne said. 'They left the Shaftesbury Theatre twenty minutes ago and got into a taxi. That taxi belongs to me. It is now somewhere between the city and your home in Guildford. The fog is supposed to be delaying them, but in fact the driver is waiting for me to give him permission to continue with his journey. If you do as I tell you they will get home unharmed, but if either of you make one false move then they will be involved in what will appear to be a motor accident.'

'You wouldn't do that,' she said in horror.

Milne twisted his mouth contemptuously.

'Please, Miss Manning, don't be naive.'

'How are we to know you are telling the truth?' Fletcher asked. He didn't doubt that Milne was capable of any atrocity, but he could still be bluffing.

Milne turned to Timovitch. 'Watch them carefully,' he said.

Timovitch put away his pipe and stood up.

'Come with me,' Milne said to Fletcher and Susan Manning.

Fletcher was still dazed from the blow to his head and his legs felt weak, but with Susan Manning he followed Milne into the adjoining room. It was a small room, fitted with a radio short wave transmitter and receiver. On the wall was a map with various location points marked with coloured pins.

Fletcher looked hard at the radio set and map. Not only was it the nerve centre of the taxi service, but also the spy ring. Now he knew how they had been passing and receiving messages from Moscow.

As if reading his thoughts Milne remarked casually: 'It has only a short range, but far enough for our trawlers to pick up any messages.' He threw a switch and picked up a microphone. 'This is control,' he said. 'What is your exact location, Robens?'

'I am slowly travelling along the Kingston Bypass towards Guildford. It is very foggy.'

'Who are your passengers?'

'I have a lady and her son. I picked them up at the Shaftesbury Theatre and I am taking them to Guildford.'

'You know what you have to do?'

There was a slight pause.

'Yes, chief.'

Milne switched off.

'Do you want any further proof?' he asked.

'You beast!' Susan said. 'You beast!'

'Take them back,' Milne ordered.

Fletcher put his arm around Susan to comfort her and led her back into the office.

'What are we to do, Paul?' she asked desperately.

'Play for time,' he whispered, 'and don't give up hope. We aren't finished yet.'

Milne came over to them again.

'When you leave here,' he said, 'you will be escorted to a lane which runs from the rear of the garage to the main road. You will both walk down that lane together and hail the first taxi which appears. The taxi will stop and you will get in. If you make one wrong move you will never see your brother again.'

'You swine,' Fletcher growled.

'Let us not be melodramatic, Fletcher.'

Milne looked at his watch.

'Five minutes,' he said.

Fletcher felt helpless. So long as Lady Manning was in that taxi they were trapped. Their only hope was that an opportunity to make a break would present itself before they were forced on the plane. He also felt annoyed with himself for walking straight into their trap. He had gained absolutely nothing by escaping from them in Oxford Street. He had been completely taken in.

'You appear to have all the trump cards, Milne,' he said.

Milne smiled.

'We had planned it all very carefully. This has not happened by accident.'

'She was an accident,' Fletcher said, meaning Susan Manning.

'We had allowed for all possibilities.'

'But she will be missed?' Fletcher persisted.

'Fletcher, you sound like a hero in a third rate novel trying to inveigle a confession out of the villain.'

Mikolyn laughed, so did Milne.

'I admit that there are one or two things which puzzle me,' Fletcher said, ignoring the sarcasm.

'Such as?' Milne asked.

'Her,' Fletcher said.

'A note has already been sent to her stepmother, in what appears to be her own handwriting, saying that she is going on a trip with a very close friend and telling them not to worry about her. By the time they start to become anxious it will be too late. We only need twenty-four hours.'

'But what then?' Fletcher asked. 'The British Government is hardly likely to let the matter rest and kidnapping innocent people is not in the rules, Milne. Not even in our game.'

'There are no rules,' Milne snarled. 'You British treat it as a game. We don't and neither do the Americans. But to ease your mind let me give you the picture. You will both be seen freely getting into a taxi, tomorrow you will be seen in Paris and then Berlin. That will be your last public appearance for a while, but rest assured there will be no nuclear conflict over you. There will be plenty of people who will step forward and testify that they saw you. The public are funny that way and their imagination can get the better of them. One or two will even have seen you on the night ferry. Naturally we will have to encourage this. When the hue and cry settles down you will again be put on show in Russia, but by then you will have had the benefit of our persuasive treatment.' He pierced his eyes and added confidentially: 'And we can be very persuasive even in such a short time.'

He gave a low rumbling laugh.

'You see, Fletcher. You are defecting. You have seen the injustices of this decadent system and are defecting. It should make very interesting reading, especially as you are taking with you, not only a copy of the British plans, which it will appear Sir Joseph has given you, but also his daughter.'

Fletcher listened aghast. It was a diabolical plan, but he knew it could work. They had perfected the art of mind-bending far beyond the comprehension of the man in the street. It wouldn't take them long to mould Susan and him into their way of thinking. He shuddered at the thought.

'And one further point,' Milne said. 'You are both going to get married. — in Russia of course!' He laughed almost hysterically. Then he turned to Tonya. 'What do you think of that, Comrade?'

Fletcher looked at her, but she ignored him.

'She is welcome to him,' she said contemptuously.

Milne laughed again.

'It is not often a man has two wives in such a short period.'

Fletcher looked at Susan. She was as white as a sheet. She looked as if she was going to faint so he put his arm around her to steady her.

Quickly he got Milne on to another tack.

'So you have a copy of the operation?' he asked.

Milne said nothing.

'Not from Sir Joseph?' Fletcher persisted.

Again Milne said nothing.

'How did you discover my identity?' Fletcher asked.

This time Milne was more informative. He appeared to get a great delight in discussing the subject.

'The mistake you made, Fletcher,' he said knowingly, 'was to meddle in the arrangements we had made to deal with Buckley. If you hadn't interfered you would probably have got away with it. But you had to try to help him. As soon as we knew the timings had been changed we were suspicious of you. Colonel Reitsler and also Comrade Sklevosky had reported doubts about you. This was not forgotten, so we checked back on you.

'Two things came to light. The remains of a mangled body in a railway tunnel in Bulgaria and a discrepancy between your medical documents and Nickovitch's originals. No two men are exactly alike, Fletcher. You can alter your features to look like someone else, but you can't make everything the same. Your fingerprints were different, so was your blood group — need I say more? After that it was only a question of time and money before we got your true identity.'

Fletcher had been aware of the differences. They had done all the obvious things, facial appearance, hair, scars, identification marks, even teeth, but as Milne had pointed out there were some things it was impossible to change. They had debated the question of whether to leave Nickovitch's documents alone, or whether to substitute a set to cover Fletcher's differences and they had decided on the latter. It had been a calculated risk. They had anticipated a thorough medical check-up somewhere along the line and could not afford to leave any loopholes. They had not anticipated his documents being checked with Nickovitch's originals in Moscow.

'Did it take you long to find out?' Fletcher asked. He had a special reason for wanting to know.

Milne boastfully gave him the details.

'Within twenty-four hours we knew you were not Nickovitch. Three days later we knew your true identity,' he said.

Before Tonya had let him make love to her, Fletcher thought. Then why had she done that? Why? He glanced across at her, but the look on her face gave him no clue as to the answer.

'My interference was of no avail,' Fletcher said, taking advantage of Milne's over confident and talkative mood.

'As it turned out, it wasn't,' Milne agreed. 'Fortunately for us Buckley's secretary phoned your message to him through to the Ministry and naturally we were informed. We arranged for one of our taxis to take him to his home to collect his car and on the way...' He made a gesture with his hands which left no doubt what had taken place in the taxi.

Susan gave a stifled gasp at Milne's confession of murder, but Fletcher was thinking of something else. Buckley had not phoned his office as his secretary had expected, so she had phoned the Ministry to pass on a message to him. According to Milne, that message had been intercepted. Unwittingly, Milne had confirmed that someone at the Ministry was giving them all their information. Somebody had informed Milne of the message and that somebody had also given them a copy of Operation Pipeline.

Who was it? It wasn't Sir Joseph, that was now obvious. That narrowed the field down. There wouldn't be many who had access to Operation Pipeline especially as the Minister had not even reported on it to the full cabinet. There would be very few … very few.

If he discounted Sir Joseph and possibly the Minister, that left only Langford and Prentice… Langford and Prentice. He mentally reflected their names. Both of them were in a position to be consulted, to even have a copy of the operation. Both knew Sir Joseph intimately and both had been at Sir Joseph's cocktail party and could have reported back on Fletcher's movements.

Something clicked inside his brain. On the day in question when the message had been phoned through, Langford had been in Aden on a fact finding mission. That left only Prentice! It had to be him.

'Prentice!' he said aloud, 'My God! Prentice.'

Milne swung around, a flash of anger on his face.

'It is time to go,' he snapped and turned to Timovitch. 'You know what to do?'

'Yes, Comrade.'

Prentice, Fletcher thought. Prentice of all people. The man who ran the department for his political masters. The stone-faced, uncommunicative, inscrutable civil servant. The man who would always be there, no matter what political upheavals or changes took place. No wonder the Russians had wanted to protect him so jealously. He was a big fish indeed. There had been no need for Milne to confirm or deny Fletcher's accusation. The look on his face had given Fletcher his answer. Prentice.

'They must not escape this time,' Milne ordered.

'They won't, Comrade. I promise you.'

Timovitch left the room and Mikolyn came over to Fletcher and Susan Manning. He waved his automatic.

'Let's go,' he said.

As they followed him out of the room Milne gave them a further warning.

'Remember. One slip and her family will suffer.'

Mikolyn led them out of the garage to a narrow lane. Milne followed behind. The lane ran between two high brick buildings and at the far end Fletcher could just make out the hazy lights of the main street. One of the buildings was a cinema and from an open door came a loud booming voice.

'You walk down there,' Milne said pointing down the lane, 'and get the first taxi. I have a man watching you at the far end so don't try anything funny.' As a parting gesture he put on his friendly, benevolent act. 'Goodbye to you both. I do hope you have a pleasant journey.'

'You haven't seen the last of us,' Fletcher snapped.

'Get going,' Mikolyn snarled and brandished his gun.

Fletcher took hold of Susan Manning's arm and together they walked down the lane. His head was still throbbing, but he could think clearly.

'We must get away from them before they get us on their plane,' he said quietly.

'But what about Peter?' Susan asked desperately.

'It will take well over an hour to get us to the plane and by that time he will be safely home.'

They were approaching the main road now.

'When I make a move,' he said, 'you must run for your life. Anything is better than ending up in one of their camps. Anything.'

'They are armed,' she whispered.

'A revolver is only accurate at very close range.' He gripped her arm. 'You must run.'

At the end of the lane they stopped. The cinema entrance was immediately to their left and a rather bored looking commissionaire paced the pavement. On their right was a shop front and the filling station. Opposite was a row of shops and in one of them stood a man watching them.

Fletcher looked back along the lane. The far end was hidden by the fog, but he knew that Mikolyn or Milne would be somewhere down there lurking in the shadows.

One or two people emerged from the warmth of the cinema and grumbled about the fog. From around the corner came the taxi.

Fletcher put out his hand, he had to. The taxi pulled into the kerb. Timovitch was driving.

'Where to, Guv'nor?' Timovitch asked in his cockney accent.

Fletcher ignored him and opened the cab door for Susan.

'Paddington Station, Guv'nor. Right 'o,' Timovitch said in a loud voice.

When Fletcher got into the cab he saw Tonya sitting in the far corner. In her hand was a revolver.

Timovitch pulled quickly away and drove a short distance along the road and then stopped again. A few seconds later Mikolyn joined them and the journey continued. Tonya took up a position directly opposite Fletcher and Mikolyn sat in the corner. Susan Manning was hunched forward and Fletcher could see Mikolyn's revolver sticking in her back.

'Is that necessary?' Fletcher asked.

'Yes,' Mikolyn snapped, 'and it has a hair trigger.'

Fletcher turned to Tonya and saw that she was looking straight at him, also with her revolver in her hand.

'Make one move,' she hissed, 'and I will kill you.'

'Does our marriage mean so little to you?' Fletcher asked sarcastically.

'Yes,' she said, 'so little. I have loathed and detested you from the first time we met.'

But there had been one night when that had not been the case, Fletcher thought. What about that? If Milne had not been lying they had known his identity before Buckley had been murdered, so why had she let him make love to her? He looked into her eyes for a glimmer of hope, but they were ice cold and unyielding. He wasn't going to get any help from her.

He sat back in his seat and turned his attentions to the route they were taking, but the fog still lingered, making it virtually impossible for him to recognise any landmarks. However, when they reached Watford the fog lifted, leaving a clear moonlit sky and Fletcher caught a glimpse of a signpost to Aylesbury.

They were only a few miles out of Watford when a crackling voice came over a radio receiver in the cab beside Timovitch.

'All clear at Watford,' the voice said.

Fletcher begrudgingly had to admire their efficiency. They were using their short wave radio link between their taxis to control their journey. They appeared to have thought of everything.

He tried to draw Tonya or Mikolyn into conversation, but Mikolyn threatened to silence him and as he didn't want another crack on the head he joined the others in their silence.

When they reached Aylesbury he glanced at his watch. It was eleven-forty. Lady Manning and her son should be safely home. But whether they were or not, he was determined to make a break for it. He wasn't going to give in without a fight. He had meant it when he had said to Susan Manning that anything was better than ending up in one of their 'experimental' camps and that included a bullet in the back.

They passed through Aylesbury and left on the Oxford road. There was no sign of any fog now.

'Two police cars heading for Aylesbury at great speed!'

The voice on the radio set repeated its urgent message.

The news electrified the atmosphere and Fletcher's hopes soared. He had written off British Security and the police, but he had underestimated them. They were coming after them.

'Faster!' Mikolyn yelled in Russian.

But Timovitch didn't need any second bidding. He was driving the cab as fast as it would go.

Tonya's eyes flashed from Fletcher to Mikolyn and back to Fletcher again. The message had shaken them, Fletcher could tell. Mikolyn shuffled in his seat impatiently.

Fletcher felt Susan's hand in his and gave her a reassuring grip. If the police were chasing them from London they would be in contact with the local force in Aylesbury and Oxford. One of them must surely intercept them.

'How much further?' Mikolyn asked.

Timovitch shouted from his cab. 'We turn off soon.'

Tonya smiled.

'They will not get here in time,' she said for Fletcher's benefit.

A short distance further on Timovitch swung the cab on to a side road and with headlights full on drove the vehicle at a furious speed.

Another message came over the radio: 'Police cars leaving Aylesbury.'

Timovitch slowed down and peered out of his cab window as if looking for a sign.

'We are here,' he yelled suddenly and turned off the road into a clearing in a thicket and came to a halt.

'Where is the plane?' Mikolyn asked frantically.

'Calm down,' Tonya snapped. 'It will be here.'

Timovitch flashed his headlights three times and they all waited tensely for a reply to his signal. In the distance a light flickered.

'Good,' Timovitch said. He turned to face Mikolyn. 'Can you manage now?' he asked.

'What are you going to do?' Mikolyn asked in surprise.

'I must get clear of the area before the police get here. There isn't very much time. You must hurry.'

Mikolyn opened the door and pulled Susan out with him. He was still holding her arm when Fletcher got out.

In the distance an aeroplane engine coughed into life. Timovitch ran forward and placed a lamp at the edge of the field, then returned to his cab.

'Walk up to the lamp,' Tonya ordered.

Fletcher and Susan walked forward. Susan tripped over a small shrub and Fletcher picked her up.

'When I make a move — run,' he whispered hurriedly.

Behind them Timovitch had reversed the taxi and was driving back along the narrow road. In front of them they could hear the plane getting nearer. Mikolyn was holding Susan now, his gun in his free hand. Tonya had her gun pointing at Fletcher's back.

The police weren't going to make it in time, Fletcher thought. If he was going to give Susan her chance of escaping it was now or never. He swung round and leapt on Mikolyn.

'Run,' he yelled as Mikolyn let go of her. 'Run!'

He landed on top of Mikolyn just as he fired. The bullet tore into Fletcher's thigh like a red hot poker, tearing at every nerve in his leg and draining all the fire out of his body.

As he rolled off Mikolyn's body, he saw the revolver pointing at him and a sadistic smile on Mikolyn's face. Desperately, he tried to move away from the pointing revolver. Crack! Crack! Two further shots rang out.

But it was Tonya who fired, not Mikolyn. And it was Mikolyn who gave a grunt and lurched forward — dead!

For a brief second time stood still. Fletcher looked at Mikolyn's body a few feet away from him in amazement, almost disbelieving what he saw. Susan had not run away, as Fletcher had ordered, but stood watching, horrified.

'Tonya!' Fletcher gasped. 'Tonya!'

Susan ran over to him and knelt down beside him.

'Oh, Paul,' she cried and started to tear away the clothing from his wound.

'I'm all right,' he said desperately. 'Leave it.'

She caught the urgency in his voice and stopped.

He tried to struggle to his feet, but collapsed to the ground again. Tonya came forward, the gun still in her hand.

'Don't try to stop me,' she said hoarsely. 'Please don't make me use this again.'

Fletcher could see her face in the moonlight. It was drawn in anguish. She bent over Mikolyn and with the gun still pointing at Fletcher and Susan, felt in his pockets. The films, Fletcher thought, she was after the films. The aircraft was getting closer, there wasn't much time. He had to try to stop her.

'Tonya, don't go,' he pleaded. 'Don't go.'

She looked at him searching his face.

'Stay, Tonya,' he cried. 'You will be safe. Don't go.'

'I can't,' she half sobbed. 'I can't. I belong to them.'

Frantically, he yelled at her in her native tongue.

'You don't owe them anything,' he shouted. 'What I said that night wasn't true.'

'No,' she shouted back. 'You were right. I am one of them.'

The small bi-plane was there, swinging around, swirling the ground with its slip stream.

He made one last attempt.

'Leave the films,' he yelled furiously. 'You will never make it. They will have to shoot you down.' But his words were drowned by the roar of the engine.

Tonya ran forward to the plane. She had given them their freedom, but she was taking a copy of the British plans with her. He had failed.

He saw her climb into the plane and felt the full force of the driving wind against his face as it moved away from them. He felt dazed, numbed. Why had she shot Mikolyn and then not stayed? Why?

'We must get help,' Susan said quietly. She dragged him on to his feet, but even with her support he couldn't move. His leg hung like a useless weight tied to his body and he was getting weaker from the loss of blood as each minute passed.

'It's no good,' he whispered. 'You go. Leave me here.'

She gave a stifled cry.

'Go, Susan,' he pleaded.

He collapsed to the ground as she ran for help. Why had Tonya done it? he kept asking himself. Why did she go? That night when she had voiced her doubts had not been an act. She had meant what she had said and he had been too blind, too cautious and too suspicious, to recognise the truth.

He had been a fool. He could have helped her and saved everything he had been working for, but he had failed her and now he was going to have to kill her. She had a copy of the plans with her, so she had to be stopped. He had to see that she didn't cross the channel.

He was only just conscious when the headlights from a car illuminated the ground around him. It registered in his numbed brain, but made no impact. Not even did the return of Susan, or the man with her, make any visible impression.

'Darling, you will be all right now,' Susan said gently.

'Thank God you're safe, Fletcher,' a man's voice said. It was a familiar voice. It was Ian Grey! 'I thought we were going to be too late.'

There was no surprise on Fletcher's face at Grey's presence.

No appreciation of its full significance.

'You will have to stop her,' was all he mumbled. 'She has a copy of Pipeline. You will have to stop her.'

'Don't worry about that,' Grey said. 'Let's get you to a hospital.'

Chapter Eighteen

Fletcher watched the nurse adjust the bed covers. It was now nearly twenty-four hours since he had been admitted to the hospital and in that time he had been drugged, operated on and regenerated. He felt unusually at peace. The nurse smoothed out the final wrinkles and left the room. A few seconds later Ian Grey joined him.

'Hullo, there,' Grey said cheerfully, 'I persuaded Susan to let me come in first, but she made me promise not to take up much time.'

Fletcher smiled. He had always liked Ian Grey.

'Tonya?' he asked politely. 'What happened?'

'If you mean your so-called wife,' Grey said, 'she is probably in Moscow by now. Any rate, somewhere behind the iron curtain.'

Fletcher was stunned.

'But she had the photostats of Operation Pipeline,' Fletcher said.

Grey gave a broad grin.

'Agreed. That was why we didn't stop her. We wanted them to have it. If they accept pipeline as being valid and act on it, we will have pulled off something really worthwhile. Our plans are entirely different. We learned our lesson at Suez.'

Fletcher felt even more at peace. Tonya had not been shot down. She was still alive and in her own country and they couldn't harm her. She had fulfilled her obligations to her masters and Britain's interests had not been jeopardised.

'What about Lady Manning and her son? Are they safe?'

'Yes, everything is neatly tied up now.'

'Everything?' Fletcher asked.

'Yes,' he said. 'Everything.'

'Even Prentice?' Fletcher asked quietly.

Grey sighed.

'Yes, even Prentice.'

He brought out a newspaper from his overcoat pocket and handed it to Fletcher. It was an evening paper, folded to display the black print of a secondary headline.

'Civil Servant killed in car crash.'

Fletcher read on.

'James Howard Prentice, a senior civil servant in the Ministry of Defence and his chauffeur, Henry Jackson, were both killed early this morning when the car they were travelling in was involved in a motor accident. The accident took place…'

Fletcher put the newspaper down. He had read enough. Prentice had been tried, found guilty and sentence had been carried out. There would be no scandal, no sackings, no political side effects, no drawn out inquiry and no publicity.

But even to Fletcher it appeared too drastic, too callous.

'He would have preferred it that way,' Grey said, as if reading Fletcher's mind.

'To be killed?' Fletcher grunted.

'Yes,' Grey said seriously. 'It had to be. Besides all the political implications and ballyhoo, it was better for his family. They will be well taken care of and no one will ever get to know the truth.'

Fletcher let the matter drop, there was a lot of truth in what Grey had just said. As for Timovitch, Fletcher felt no remorse, only respect. He was a professional and knew the rules.

'How long have you known?' he asked.

'Well, we have known there was a leak at the top for some time and by a long process of elimination we pinned it down to the Ministry of Defence and four men in particular. The Minister himself, Sir Joseph Manning, Langford and Prentice. When you turned up we realised the pace was hotting up and we were on the right track, so we kept a very close watch on your movements.

'Your meetings with Jackson came to light and also his with the Continental Travel Agency. We have had our suspicions about that firm for a long time, but we had nothing on the Grants. The Minister, Sir Joseph and Langford, all used the agency and had met the Grants socially.

'Only Prentice had no contact with them, but when he went on holiday last August two of our men went with him and who should turn up at his isolated resort but the Grants. This was suspicious, especially when they had no further social contacts when they both returned home. We felt certain the Grants were involved, so we brought them out into the open. We didn't know whether you knew of their existence.'

Fletcher frowned. 'Buckley,' he muttered.

'Yes, Buckley,' Grey said, 'but don't reproach yourself. He knew the risk he was taking and he knew what they intended to do. Unfortunately, at the time none of us knew about Curtis and the Avon Garage in Hendon.'

The name was unfamiliar to Fletcher, but he gathered he was referring to Milne.

'I think I know who killed him,' Fletcher said quietly.

'Who?' Grey asked abruptly.

'Vincent, alias Andrea Mikolyn.'

'What makes you so sure?'

Fletcher shrugged. He had no proof. It was only a hunch — a hunch based on Tonya's actions. She had liked Buckley and his murder had genuinely shocked her, but she had shown no remorse when she killed Mikolyn. It made Fletcher think that his freedom had not been the only motive for her shooting. But Grey wanted facts.

'No particular reason,' was all he said and changed the subject. 'How did you get on to Curtis?'

'When we back checked on Buckley's movements the trail took us to the Avon Garage so we put a close watch on it. It wasn't long before our monitoring unit caught them sending out coded messages to be relayed to Moscow. As you know everything is controlled by the Kremlin. We now took another look at our suspects. They all used taxis belonging to Curtis, but Prentice and the Grants always used the same one. It was now obvious that the taxi was being used for passing information and orders between Prentice, the Grants and Curtis.'

'Is that how Prentice passed on his copy of Pipeline?'

'Yes, soon after the Minister had held his meeting, he took a taxi ride and needless to say the taxi returned immediately to the Garage.'

'And the act with Sir Joseph was to throw the suspicion on to him when the leak became public?'

'It would appear so,' Grey agreed. 'If the leak had been genuine all hell would have been let loose and everything would have pointed to Sir Joseph. I doubt if he could have convinced his closest friends it was a frame up, especially when all concerned would have been looking for a scapegoat.'

'How did you manage to pass on the rejected plans?' Fletcher asked.

'We realised the time was ripe for them to act, the international scene was so critical. If they were going to make a move it had to be now or never. Originally we had four suspects, but by now we were pretty certain Prentice was our man. Also, the P.M. personally vouched for the Minister, he wouldn't even entertain the possibility of him being a traitor and naturally we had to accept his word.

'At any rate, the chief met the P.M. immediately he arrived back from the States and got him to play ball. The P.M. had with him the plans agreed with the Americans to meet the Russian threat in the Middle East. He was persuaded to keep them personally until he met his cabinet this morning. He agreed to do this and also to carry out our plan to catch Prentice.

'As soon as he arrived at Downing Street, he passed on our orders to the Minister. Sir Joseph was to be told to prepare a detailed report on the present commitments of the armed forces with a view to releasing troops for a move in the Middle East. He was to have his report available for the P.M.'s conference.

'Prentice was to be given a copy of Operation Pipeline — which incidentally was the brainchild of the army Staff College — and asked to give his personal views and comments before the Minister reported to the Prime Minister the following morning. Prentice was told that this was the plan intended to be put into operation and also that both Sir Joseph and Langford were also preparing a similar report on the same operation. Langford, however, was told to prepare a report on the political effects, both at home and abroad, of an armed intervention in the Middle East.

'The Minister followed his instructions implicitly, we saw to that. Neither party came in contact with the other and each party was given the full treatment about security and the secret nature of their work. Only Prentice was told what the other two were supposed to be doing so that he would feel safe to pass on the information, but he in fact was the only one to have access to Operation Pipeline. He fell for the trap and took his customary taxi ride. After that you were contacted and went through your little pantomime. You gave us quite a headache at one stage, though.'

'When was that?'

'When you jumped out of the car in Oxford Street. It was quite a relief when you turned up at the garage again.'

'You saw me there?'

'Well, one of my men did. The commissionaire at the cinema.'

'I thought he looked rather bored,' Fletcher said and added critically. 'You took a long time to close in.'

'Yes, I agree,' Grey admitted thoughtfully, 'we nearly slipped up there. It was the damned fog. The trouble was we weren't too sure how they intended to get it out of the country. It was just possible they would pass it through their embassy as time was so important and if that was the case we wanted to be aware of it. I suppose we were being too clever. Any rate, we have our hands full watching the various embassy officials when you went shooting off north in that taxi. We realised what they had in mind, but of course the blasted fog held us back. Sorry about that.'

'That's all right,' Fletcher muttered. 'It was probably just as well.' He was thinking of Tonya and Susan. If Grey had arrived on the scene earlier it might have had a different ending for both of them.

'How did Susan become involved?' he asked.

'She became suspicious of Vincent. A few years ago Susan actually visited Australia and is consequently well informed about the country. One or two of his remarks didn't tie up.'

'Did she tell the authorities?'

'Fortunately, she only told Buckley and he promised to look into the matter. He also persuaded her not to tell her father.

We weren't too sure about him at the time and we didn't want Susan raising the alarm. She stopped seeing Vincent, but after Buckley's death she decided to take matters into her own hands. Although Buckley had told her that he had checked up on Vincent and found nothing suspicious, she wasn't convinced. She made some enquiries through some friends in Australia and the answers she got made her realise Vincent was an impostor.'

'But not a spy?'

'No, I think she thought he was some sort of fake. On the night you went to visit Sir Joseph, Vincent had orders to keep her out of the way. They wanted a clear field for you to see Sir Joseph, they must have realised she was suspicious and didn't want her raising any alarms when you were with Sir Joseph. Susan naturally wasn't keen to see Vincent and in fact spurned his invitation to join him.

'Vincent became desperate. He knew that Susan usually worked late at her father's private office attending to his correspondence, so he turned up there just as she was about to leave. Again he suggested that she joined him for the evening, but Susan insisted she was going home. Vincent became belligerent and they had a row.

'During their row Susan confronted him with her suspicions. Vincent must have been badly shaken, but he ridiculed her suggestions and managed to bluff it out. Eventually he managed to persuade her to let him take her to the station. Needless to say they never got to the station and she ended up in the garage instead.'

'Poor girl,' Fletcher said. 'She never knew what hit her.'

'Well, it hasn't had any lasting effects. Incidentally, I had to tell her certain facts but not everything. I would appreciate it if you would do the same.'

'I understand.'

The two men sat looking at each other for a while, each to his own thoughts.

Fletcher broke the silence.

'My money was on Langford,' he said. 'He seemed to have most to gain.'

'You weren't alone there. He headed our list for a long time.'

'Or Davies,' Fletcher added.

'Davies?' Grey asked. 'Why Davies?'

'I was told to make his acquaintance. He was considered a useful man to know and I must say he was very friendly.'

'H'm,' Grey muttered, 'Davies is like that, but we have nothing on him.'

'Did Sir Joseph have any other visitors last night before I arrived?' Fletcher asked.

'Only your wife. She spent the afternoon with Lady Manning and had tea at their house in Guildford. She left at the same time Lady Manning and her son went to the theatre.'

'By taxi?'

'Yes.'

So it was Tonya who had been in the other taxi in Richmond Park, Fletcher thought. She had met Timovitch to give him a last minute report on Sir Joseph and to confirm that Lady Manning and her son were out of the way. He had all the answers now — except one.

'Why did Prentice do it?' he asked thoughtfully.

Grey looked serious.

'Only Prentice could tell you that,' he said. 'Who knows what goes on in the minds of such people? Once they are converted to the communist's cause they become arrogant, dogmatic, fanatical and blind. They are like drug addicts, convinced that their new found cause is the only saviour for the world.' He gave a long sigh. 'One thing is certain,' he said, 'they are the most difficult to uncover.'

'It could have been caused through a combination of frustration and envy,' Fletcher said.

'Or any hidden suppression,' Grey agreed, 'but we will never know.'

There was an impatient tapping at the door.

'That will be Susan,' Grey said. 'I did promise I wouldn't be long.' He stood up. 'I'll get a man down in the morning to get your report. I want every single detail.'

'It will make interesting reading,' Fletcher said dryly.

The two men shook hands and Grey left to complete his work, but not before he had escorted Susan Manning in to the room.

She came and sat on the bed, close to Fletcher.

She smiled and their eyes met. Fletcher had never seen her look so beautiful before.

'Now that you are not married...' she whispered.

Fletcher held out his arms and gently pulled her towards him.

Chapter Nineteen

'Passengers for the British European Airways Flight No. 264 for Athens…'

The announcement continued, but Fletcher had stopped listening. The time had come for him to leave, to return home. He had given Grey all the facts, he had answered all their questions and he had discussed his future with his superiors. Soon he was to take up a staff appointment controlling the work of their agents in the Middle East from one of the embassies, but first he had work to do. The Middle East was still in a turmoil despite the Russians' loss of influence in the area.

The Russians had fallen into the trap and cried wolf. They had shown their iron claws and made the cardinal mistake of moving troops over their border in anticipation of a similar British move. Their move had electrified the Middle East.

Overnight the uprising in Iran ceased to exist and a wave of national unity swept the country. The Arab countries had united in condemning the Russians and had even rescinded their previous treaty of mutual aid. For once the Russians were the Imperialistic aggressors and in face of such hostility they had hastily retreated across their borders.

In the game of international power chess it had been the West's turn to call 'checkmate'.

Fletcher turned to the small party who had come to see him off.

Ian Grey and Sir Joseph shook his hand warmly. It was not the end of their friendship, only the beginning. He would be seeing them both again. Sir Joseph had been full of gratitude for what Fletcher had done and full of self-criticism of his own blindness. But it had made him a lot wiser of what was going on under the surface and in future he would be a more useful servant of his country.

Lady Manning kissed him tenderly. She, more than anyone, had been badly shaken by the turn of events. She had formed a deep affection for Tonya and Fletcher was pleased to see that she still did not speak ill of her.

Susan was the last to say farewell. She put her arms around him and whispered, 'If you haven't sent for me by Easter, darling, I will come out and start a war of my own.'

On the plane, Fletcher relaxed in his seat and fastened his safety belt.

Casually he glanced around him, his critical eye weighing up the passengers in his immediate vicinity. He saw the two Turkish students, the elderly lady and her younger companion, the two businessmen, the stout man with the short grey beard, the English family and the attractive air hostess.

For a brief second his eyes returned to the stout man with the beard. He had a rough, tanned, friendly face and his large hands were resting on his stomach as if he were contemplating some gastronomical delight.

Fletcher smiled knowingly and turned his attention to his side window. He was indeed going home.

A NOTE TO THE READER

If you have enjoyed the novel enough to leave a review on **Amazon** and **Goodreads**, then we would be truly grateful.

Sapere Books is an exciting new publisher of brilliant fiction and popular history.

To find out more about our latest releases and our monthly bargain books visit our website:
saperebooks.com

Printed in Great Britain
by Amazon

34154740R00125